THE WORLD BENEATH THE CITY

The World Beneath the City

ROBERT DALEY

J. B. LIPPINCOTT COMPANY
PHILADELPHIA
AND NEW YORK

Library of Congress Catalog Card No. 59–13081

Printed in the United States of America

To A. J.

Contents

Illustrations

THE WORLD BENEATH THE CITY

1. Under the Sidewalks of New York

UNDER THE CITY, under the feet of bustling executives, gawking tourists, trench diggers, under the wheels of taxis, buses and trucks, lie the unseen roots which nourish New York. Without them the city could not exist. They are roots of incredible complexity and awesome power.

There are 7,000 miles of gas mains, 5,000 miles of sewers, 2,200 miles of TV cables and 15,000,000 miles of telephone wires—enough to circle this planet six hundred times. Subway trains, 8,700 of them a day, thunder along 726 miles of track. There are 87 miles of high pressure steam lines for tasks as varied as pressing trousers and heating skyscrapers, steam pressured to 150 pounds per square *inch*, cooked to 1,000° Fahrenheit and driven through concrete reinforced pipes at nearly three hundred miles an hour. Some 19,000 miles of electrical cables bristle with current boosted to 69,000 volts (the normal wall outlet is 120 volts). Ordinary water courses through 5,528 miles of mains under such intense pressure that a single leak could cause the loss of 3,000,000 gallons a day.

All of the city's veins and arteries are troublemakers except the telephone cables. ("You could grab fifty of them and receive no more than a mild shock," said a New York Telephone Company official.) Malfunction of only a portion could cause panic and paralysis—if the water supply failed for instance—or even widespread destruction.

Under Fifth Avenue and Forty-ninth Street, one calm afternoon, accumulated sewer gas exploded, shattering a manhole cover and sending grenade-like fragments in all directions. Miraculously, no one was hurt. In Brooklyn as many as eight 70-pound covers were blown into the air by a single explosion, and once a little boy was crushed when a 200-pound cover came down on top of him.

Burst water mains have flooded subways, isolated bank vaults, stalled elevators and caused floating bargains in department store basements. Vast midtown areas have been made to resemble paddy fields in summer, curb-to-curb skating rinks in winter. Pavement has been undermined until whole sections —with an occasional car on top—have suddenly dropped eight feet below street level. Once a car, having just sheared off a fire hydrant, was found standing on its nose, its hindquarters supported by the force of the cannonading column of water.

Cigarettes have rolled into Consolidated Edison trenches, causing gas mains to blow up thunderously. Then they burn, a fiercely compelling spectacle.

Steam lines have burst underground, melting street asphalt to the consistency of mud, in which cars sank to their hubcaps while dazed drivers gaped uncomprehendingly. At Union Square one burst into the air a few summers ago, a geyser shooting forty stories high which, in its brief moment in the sun, rivaled Old Faithful for glory.

"New York is only six hundred square miles," noted a Con Edison executive, "but it's one of the great concentrations of power on the face of the globe."

The power which lies under the city demands constant attention. On guard round the clock is a small army of elite technicians and laborers, upwards of twenty thousand men whose sunless world is entered via 683,000 manholes which belong to half a dozen companies and sub-companies and whose covers are "fingerprinted" (lettered) accordingly. They are a well-paid, clannish crew, sometimes given to picturesque figures of speech. "It's as crowded under the streets as a plate of spagetti," said one worker. "In some areas," remarked another, "you can't dig with anything bigger than a tablespoon."

They have learned to anticipate trouble. When July heat

causes every air conditioner in town to be switched on at once, manholes must be packed with dry ice and perforated garden hose thrust through conduits in an effort to cool cables which would otherwise burn out.

Water mains, many of them upwards of a century old, burst on the average of once a day, usually at night when the city's faucets are shut and pressure has built up. The record is six in five hours, flooding the Metropolitan Opera House area one November midnight in 1957. On such occasions the men must move fast, for sub-surface gushers undermine gas and steam lines which then break, causing chaotic eruptions in the streets.

Underground workers often must share their domain with other creatures: rats as big as cats in the sewers, an especially sinewy and disheveled breed of cat in some sections of the subways. Many of the cats never have seen the light of day. They are fed by trackwalkers, grow abnormally quick at jumping out of the way of trains, rarely are hit, but occasionally mistake exposed portions of the third rail for a safe landing place.

Sewer inspectors, searching for leaks, blockages and other trouble spots during the low tide of the midnight-to-8-AM lull, must sidestep floating drums, boxes and Christmas trees. Some have found jewelry, murder weapons, false teeth and valuable glass eyes in catch basins, or washing by in the sludge. One night one of them was shocked to find a good-sized alligator swimming languidly toward him. He bolted. In ensuing weeks dozens of alligators were hunted down and liquidated. Children had bought them as tiny pets, which harassed parents soon had flushed away. In the sewers the beasts had thrived, growing to "alarming" sizes.

Sewer inspecting is not quite the most dangerous sub-surface occupation. That dubious honor goes to those repairmen who must stand, presumably insulated, on rubber mats and tinker with live third rails while subway trains rush by as often as every ninety seconds.

Subways and utility lines run mainly under streets, rarely under sidewalks and (theoretically at least) never under buildings. The most jammed area is Herald Square and few jobs in history can match the complexity of pushing the Sixth

Avenue Subway through there in the late 1930's. At various levels fifteen tracks of the BMT, Hudson Tubes, Pennsylvania and Long Island railroads converged. The heavy utility mains and cables of the midtown area snaked this way and that. Station concourses, passageways and Gimbel's Basement further clogged the route. While work proceeded, neither street nor underground traffic, nor utility service could be interrupted, and the "roof" had to be constantly shored up because the old Sixth Avenue El ran overhead. The job was finally completed, but it is possibly significant that no new subways have been attempted since.

There is no over-all map of what is under New York. Each system has its own maps, which often are inaccurate, incomplete or both. Consolidated Edison trench diggers recently cut into twelve hundred feet of wooden conduits in Brooklyn which had been "missing" since 1932. And the company admits curiosity in the whereabouts of half a mile of conduits buried somewhere in Staten Island.

Sounding devices akin to stethoscopes are used when excavators uncover uncharted cables or mains. If the reading is negative: "We hold our breath and cut." Diggers also have turned up chests of coins, deposits of semi-precious stones, ship hulls, a British dungeon, colonial tools, weapons and utensils, even long-forgotten graveyards.

As late as 1799 New York was a village of about thirty thousand people, and there was nothing buried under its cobblestone streets except possibly some Indians. In those days the city was irrigated by two dozen tumbling streams of considerable beauty but questionable purity. The island's largest body of water was the Collect Pond, between Chambers Street and Broadway, which had become such a notorious sewer by 1811 that it was drained and filled in with what an early historian termed "good and wholesome earth"—the first of some forty-seven ponds smothered by the superstructure of the city. The drain ran northwest to the Hudson; it was later roofed over, forming a sewer wide enough for two trucks to pass abreast, the largest sewer of the New World. The street that ran above was, and is, called Canal Street.

New Yorkers take for granted the weird world beneath their feet.

Also in 1811 the aldermen adopted a plan "entirely defi-
cient in sentiment and charm." Ignoring the wooded hills
and fertile valleys of the island, they decreed that henceforth
all avenues must proceed directly north, all streets straight east
and west. Nature lovers of the day were outraged, but present-
day engineers have blessed the plan a thousand times. Without
it, the network under the city's streets would be immeasurably
more tangled than it is.

It was 1828 when the first gas street lights appeared, nourished by nine miles of iron pipes. The telephone system was
born in 1878, and four years later Thomas Edison began supplying electricity to four hundred street lamps and fifty-nine
private customers.

Water reserves had been critical since before the Revolution,
when pumps and wells were as ubiquitous as today's mailboxes.
The first water mains, in 1799, were made of hollow logs and
the water which coursed through them was practically poisonous. Today's supply comes from as far away as Kingston, New
York, through great pressure tunnels bored through solid rock
as far below the city's streets (750 feet) as the Woolworth
Building, sixth mightiest of the world's skyscrapers, towers
above.

Today New York is the greatest living, breathing organism
in the world. Once it was a collection of wigwams. It could
not grow from the one to the other until the roots which it
pushed down into earth and rock were strong enough. Thus
the story of those roots, and the men who put them there, is
the story of the city itself. It is a curious saga of inventors and
charlatans, visionaries and crooks—of Alfred Eli Beach, who
invented and built an extraordinary pneumatic subway twenty-
one feet under Broadway in 1870; of Borough President Connolly who sold the city nearly eight million dollars' worth of
non-existent sewers during the Roaring Twenties; of Aaron
Burr, whose dream of empire was bound up with water pipes,
wooden ones, beneath the streets of New York. It is the story
also of the "Smugglers'" tunnel under Brooklyn, bums living
in luxury below Park Avenue, and alligators hunted through
the sewers of Manhattan. There is "Smelly" Kelly, the subway

sniffer, whose job for over thirty years has been following his nose along subway tracks; and there is Teddy May, who worked more than half a century in the sewers and who loved them so much that he used to take long walks in them on Sunday afternoons—or so his friends said and believed.

Each time a new aqueduct or subway joined the maze under New York there was a mad, completely joyous civic celebration, most of them so splendid you would have thought a war had ended. That is part of the story too, because it is a kind of delight which does not exist in this sophisticated Atomic Age. To read about it is likely to seem strange and a little bewildering. No utility connection seems very marvelous any more; it occurs to no one that without electricity Broadway would be dark, without sewers Wall Street would become a stagnant, steaming jungle, without water the city and all within it would die. In fact nothing is quite so taken for granted by New Yorkers as the weird world beneath their very feet.

2. Aaron Burr and the Wooden Water Pipes

TO A NEW YORKER, nothing seems more natural. He turns on the tap and a jet of water spurts into the basin with the force of a geyser. Furthermore, the water is clear, cold, pure and good-tasting. Among people who study such things, New York water is said to possess these qualities in greater abundance than almost any city water anywhere.

Almost no one is aware that for more than two hundred years New York water tasted so foul that horses would not drink it, was so impure that disease decimated the population every other year, so expensive that the poor went without it and the streets were filled with filth, its sources so widely scattered that periodic fires wiped out four or five hundred houses at a clip. Travelers would not stop at New York because of the water. Drunkenness was often the solemn consideration of the Common Council—the water was so untasty that some people *always* mixed it with spirits—and how could drunkenness be stamped out? The Dutch settlers who founded the city almost gave up and moved on for want of water and when Fort Amsterdam surrendered to the British siege in 1664 there was no well or stream inside the fort. The water supply consisted of about two dozen pitched casks which had been removed from the ships in the harbor and laboriously lugged up inside the walls. These were almost empty. The Dutchmen were parched and had no more interest in a fight.

The island found by Henry Hudson and explored by the crew of the *Half Moon* in 1609 must have been one of the most beautiful spots on earth. Scenically it had everything, great bowering trees, hills, and dales, jutting granite cliffs, cool ponds. Two dozen streams, tumbling this way and that, sparkled in the sun. Majestic rivers surrounded it.

Water? There seemed to be plenty, even when the rivers were found to contain the salty backwash of the sea. What about Sunfish Pond (at Madison Avenue and Thirty-second Street)? The fish there were so enthusiastic that they jumped and splashed about like children. What about Stuyvesant and Cedar Ponds which were later to be so popular for skating and ice boating? What about the Collect Pond (near Canal Street) which was several acres in area, big enough to contain test runs of the world's first steam-powered vessel in 1796?

What the Dutch could not know was that the ponds were shallow, the streams fickle. Prolonged drought tended to dry them up. What the Dutch also did not know, was that the granite foundation of the island (that same foundation which today so admirably supports the heaviest buildings in the world) would cause the speedy ruin of any wells which might be drilled to tap subterranean springs. The geological formation, so essential to twentieth century New York, was a deadly liability to seventeenth century New Amsterdam. The rock bottom of the island was covered with alluvial deposits easily permeated by the salty rivers. There were few gushers found anyway; most well drillers became elated merely to find underground pools which could be pumped to the surface.

What drillers found were merely pools of rain water which had filtered down through the sandy soil (carrying all manner of impurities with it) and collected in depressions atop the granite hulk of the island. One of the city's favorite pumps in later years was located three feet outside the wall of the Trinity Church graveyard. The pool of rain water which this pump tapped and which the city so merrily drank, was exactly underneath the graveyard itself—and had previously laved the decomposing corpses of hundreds of former citizens who lay buried there.

Not until 1667, the British now in command, was a well

finally drilled inside Fort Amsterdam. Another was drilled outside the sally port at Bowling Green; a pump was installed,
public gardens laid out, and this became New York's first sub-
urb and first resort, a spa as renowned and popular among
those people, as Hot Springs or Carlsbad today. The water
was believed to have medicinal properties. On the lawn at
Bowling Green the men bowled (naturally), while women
sat beneath the trees sipping the water and watching their
frolicking children.

Then came the grim drought of 1672. A Lieutenant von
Krafft wrote in his diary: "This afternoon our foragers and
sharpshooters returned. They had measured at the camp but
could find no water on account of the great heat of this year
which had dried up everything." By September 4, well diggers
had drilled down forty feet, but had found no water. Three
weeks more passed without rain. "There is the general complaint," noted Von Krafft, "that all would soon die for want
of water."

The crisis passed, but the Common Council met and ordained that "severall weells bee made in the places hereafter
menconed (for the publique good of the cytie) by the inhabitants of Each Streete where the said wells shall bee made.
Opposite butcher Roeoliff Johnson's in Broadway opposite
Hendrick Van Dykes, in Smith Streete opposite John Cavileers,
and in Water Streete opposite Cornelius Van Borsums." The
first stone well was also to be built in the back yard of City
Hall. Within ten years nine more wells were ordered, "one
half the cost to be paid by the streete one half by the citty."

By this time the danger of fires was acute. If they did start,
they usually blazed until there was nothing left in their paths
to burn. Most of the city's homes had thatched roofs; their
chimneys were of wood or twigs matted with clay.

In 1648, the city then twenty-two years old, an ordinance
had been passed forbidding wooden chimneys between the fort
and the river. Money from fines levied against violaters was
sent to Holland to purchase ladders for the eight-man vol-
unteer fire department. By law there were 250 filled leather
buckets in the town at all times, but in winter (when all householders had fires on the hearth and when most conflagrations

started) these buckets were often frozen solid. So was water in the wells. The first fireman on the scene of a blaze usually jumped down into the nearest well with an ax and chopped away surface ice.

Appalled at the toll of fires, the Council next passed a law that all haystacks and thatched roofs had to be removed within four months, "henhouses and hogpens included." It was also decided to send to Holland for more leather buckets. Instead, the shoemakers' union met and, having determined that it was time for the New World to stand on its own feet, commissioned two of its number to pound out the new buckets themselves.

Under the British in 1687, it was ordained that there be one filled bucket for every two hearths. Bakers were obliged to keep three on hand, brewers six. The owners' names were always painted on the buckets which, naturally, got badly mixed up whenever a fire reached bucket-brigade proportions. Thus it became the job of the town crier to make the rounds after every fire, shouting that the exchange of buckets would take place in such and such a place at such and such a time. These people owned very little apart from food and livestock, there was little money in circulation, and the loss of a bucket would have been a major calamity—it could not easily have been replaced.

By 1700, pumps had been mounted above many of the wells, and soon an act was passed "for mending publick wells" and for overseers whose duty it was to repair and guard the pumps. This was necessary because the same kind of person who today turns in false alarms spent his time in those days cutting the ropes which dangled buckets into the wells, or smashing pump handles or committing other nuisances.

Meanwhile, the water was no tastier than before, fires had become ever more prevalent, and in 1731 the city fathers sent to England for two hand-pumped fire "Ingens" which could squirt, it was said, a jet of water upon the blaze. A few years later the New York Fire Department was organized, forty "strong, able, discreet, honest and sober men," who became exempt from the militia, from jury duty and from other functions, by promising to be on hand whenever tongues of flame showed through the trees of the city and the horrifying cry of "FIRE!" was shouted from the lookout towers.

By the middle of the eighteenth century, New York well water was so evil-tasting that it had become notorious. A traveler, Peter Kalm, wrote: "The want of good water lies heavy upon the horses of the strangers that come to this place, for they do not like to drink the water from the wells of the town."

The only good water came from a spring a short distance from town, in what is now Park Row, between Baxter and Mulberry streets. A pump soon was placed over this spring, and the water sold to those who could afford it, for their tea and other beverages. Ornamental grounds were laid out around the pump, which was called Tea-water Pump Garden. This became a popular resort, the citizens sitting outdoors under the trees, sipping tea and other beverages made with this water, which was vastly superior to what they were used to.

This well was twenty feet deep, about four feet in diameter, and there was never more or less water in it than three feet in depth. It was estimated that 110 hogsheads of water were taken from it during the winter months, and about 216 in summer when the population had a thirst which less tasty water failed to satisfy.

This water cost three pence a hogshead (130 gallons) at the pump, one cent a gallon at your door. "Tea-water men" drove about the city, selling water from heavy casks. It was a racket and was recognized as such, but what could a person do? "Laws for the regulating of Tea-water Men" were passed in 1757, but had small effect.

At first the Tea-water pump was operated by a prodigious pump handle, which only the burliest and roughest men could operate. Later this was replaced by an apparatus activated by a pair of undernourished horses driven by a boy.

The Tea-water was the only drinkable water in town, but was controlled by a group of thugs who made outrageous profits and whose wagons, waiting their turn to pass under the pump, blocked traffic for a mile back in all directions.

Plainly something had to be done about water, particularly since the purity of the Tea-water itself was suspect. Its source was the same underground spring or springs which fed the Collect Pond, which was dangerously close. The Collect, once the pride of the city, had by 1780 become "a very sink and common sewer," where housewives scrubbed their laundry on flat stones, dumped their slop buckets, and where others disposed of dead dogs and cats.

Along came one Christopher Colles, who offered to build the city a "water works." On April 22, 1774, Colles proposed constructing a reservoir near Collect Pond. He would build his tank atop a hill, pump the water up into it by steam engines, and the force of gravity would make it flow out through hollow log pipes in any direction the Common Council in its wisdom should decide.

After three months of deliberation, the Council finally approved this plan. Augustus and Frederick van Cortlandt, the Ford Foundation of their day, forthwith donated the site— Colles had chosen a combination marsh and pond whose undergrowth was dense with game birds, and from whose dark recesses bullfrogs croaked all day long.

A group of city fathers, solemn with the responsibility which lay upon them, then went out to taste the water. This source, it seemed to them, would provide New York's water supply for generations yet unborn—for all time, probably. It was up to them to make certain that the water was of good vintage.

And so in their best coats and hats they rode their horses up to the place, dismounted, and took each one his turn at the dipper which was reached out into the pond. Each man raised the dipper to his lips, sipped it, rolled it around on his tongue, swallowed it slowly and, more slowly and deliberately still, nodded approval. Yes sir, the water was of excellent quality.

No winetaster in a cellar in Champagne ever exercised his art with greater care or scrupulousness. If, at that moment, a hunter had let fly his blunderbuss at some partridge or quail, it would have been considered an interruption of the most uncouth sort.

Having won approval, Christopher Colles went ahead with his waterworks. Orders were given for sixty thousand linear feet of pine logs, "streight and free from shakes and large knots." The logs were to be fourteen to twenty feet in length, nine inches in diameter inside, twelve inches outside. Each log was to have a "male end and a female end." The outside of the male end was to be whittled down, and the bore of the female end scooped out, so that the end of one log could be plunged into the one ahead of it and bunged tight, forming a watertight connection.

Now, behind Collect Pond, Colles began his pump house, and his great masonry reservoir which was to be thirty feet in diameter, holding twenty thousand hogsheads of water under a tile roof. Admiring citizens watched as stone was laid upon stone. The place was as formidable as a redoubt, and was soon to be used as one.

The Common Council had waited too long. Before the waterworks was completed, blood had been spilled at Lexington. Soon war came to New York as well. Work on Colles' project stopped, as Minutemen clambered behind the walls and stuck their rifles through every gap. There was no water flowing through the wooden pipes when fire struck again. In September, 1776, after the British occupied the city, a mighty conflagration consumed all of the city between Whitehall Street and Broadway. Trinity Church and 493 houses burned to the ground. When the war ended and the British finally went away, nothing was left of the waterworks but remnants of the stone structure. The reservoir was empty, the log pipes had been burned as firewood.

The Common Council had promised to pay Colles £3,600 and now he sued for the six hundred still due him, contending that he had suffered "poignant afflictions" during the war and needed cash. As is normal when people sue city hall, he got a third of what he was entitled to.

The war had lasted six years. During the decade and a half which followed, many other persons came forward with plans to supply water but the Common Council, for one reason or another, procrastinated.

In August, 1798, a terrible yellow fever epidemic descended upon the city. From a population of about thirty thousand, it exacted two thousand lives.

A witness wrote: "New York this time has got a plague indeed. . . . It seems to be admitted on all sides to be a home-bred Pestilence. The inhabitants have really poisoned their city by the accumulation of Excrement, putrid Provision and every unclean thing."

A reporter described the Collect Pond behind Tea-water pump as "a shocking hole, where all impure things center together and engender the worst of unwholesome productions; foul with excrement, frogspawn, and reptiles, that delicate pump is supplied. The water has grown worse manifestly within a few years. It is time to look out some other supply, and discontinue the use of a water growing less and less wholesome every day. . . . Can you bear to drink it on Sundays in the Summer time? It is so bad before Monday morning as to be very sickly and nauseating. . . . Plague will make a yearly slaughter until you furnish better water."

Yellow fever. No one knew what the disease was, what caused it or where it came from. But all who recorded impressions of the time mentioned unwholesome water, too little of it to wash away the accumulated filth of decades, filth which spawned "clouds of musketoes, incredibly large and distressing. . . ."

Even so, the indecisive Common Council might have ordered another survey made as to possible sources of water, and then forgotten the whole thing. But other elements were at work; they were politics and profit, in that order.

Politics in that Alexander Hamilton's Federalist Party controlled the Bank of New York. Aaron Burr's Democratic-Republican Party was without funds, and had no means of raising any. Hamilton, his party firmly seated, wealthy, bossed political New York. Burr, ambitious, cunning, unscrupulous, had to find some way to get money if he was to compete with Hamilton. Burr, then as always, intended to make himself President. Nothing was going to stand in his way.

The city needed water. Burr conceived a way to use this need. Skillfully, so carefully that even the shrewd Hamilton never caught on, Burr maneuvered a bill through the State Legislature which granted a charter to a water company which was to be called the Manhattan Company; Aaron Burr, Chairman of the Board.

It was really a lesson in politics. Burr lobbied, talked, attacked, withdrew, cajoled. When opposition to him weakened, he stimulated new opposition himsef. This was because Burr at first sponsored a bill for a *public* water company which would provide New York with the water it needed at a price it could afford, profiting no politician, only waterdrinkers—a bill entirely different from what he really wanted.

When at length the Legislature grew weary of the debate, Burr steered another bill past the legislators so fast they hardly noticed. It granted the *private* Manhattan Company rights to dam and divert the water of any stream, use the water power of any stream, dig whatever canals, lay whatever pipes it saw fit. Its powers were virtually unlimited. Furthermore, the tag end of the bill contained a little clause which made it lawful for the company to use its surplus capital in any manner "not inconsistent with the constitution and laws of this state or of the United States."

On that inoffensive little clause Aaron Burr would be able to build his bank. It must have seemed to him that day that nothing now could stop him. He would become President of the United States, an emperor if he chose, a man of unlimited power.

All he had to do was fulfill the charter, lay a few pipes, force some kind of water to flow through them. The foolish, the merely gullible, would flock to invest in the company; it would overflow with money. And that extra money could be used, according to the charter, "in any manner not inconsistent with the constitution and laws"—to start a bank, to sponsor a Presidential candidate.

Hamilton, discovering the ruse at last, fumed and raged, but it was too late. A second bank was about to be founded, to be called the Bank of the Manhattan Company. Burr could be stopped only if he infuriated the city by ignoring the water problem all together, and brought public wrath down upon his head. This Burr had no intention of doing.

Now it was April 11, 1799, and the officers of the Manhattan Company, Burr, John Watts, Richard Harrison, John B. Church and others, met at the house of innkeeper Edward Barden to decide what they should do. Burr piously affirmed that the first object of the company was water. This statement had the virtue of quieting Hamilton, and of easing the fears of those who knew Burr well enough to distrust him.

It was not until a week later that the same men met again to "consider the most proper means of employing the capital of the company."

"I've got a terrific idea," said Burr, or words to that effect. "Let's start a bank with it!"

Four months later the Bank of the Manhattan Company, with a capital stock of $2,000,000, commenced operations at 40 Wall Street, then a wooden frame building, today a stone-and-steel skyscraper housing a multi-billion-dollar enterprise. The Manhattan Company quit the water business a long time back but, now called the Chase Manhattan Bank, it is still one of the world's richest banks.

Even before the Revolution, engineers and health experts had advocated piping water into Manhattan from various Bronx and Westchester ponds and streams. This project the newly formed Manhattan Company refused to consider—it would divert too much capital and interfere with operations of the bank.

It was therefore proposed that a steam engine be erected on the banks of Collect Pond, which would force that water into pipes and down through the city. This plan was leaked tentatively to the press of the day, to see what public reaction would be.

New York was horrified. The Collect Pond engine might successfully clean the streets, but its operation would also expose the black, slimy muck on the bottom of the pond, as well as whatever garbage and animal corpses might be embedded there. No. No. No. Not the Collect Pond!

Caught in a bind, Burr invited suggestions. At the same time, one authority, Elias Ring, contended that the Collect was not impure at all. It had become contaminated only because streets drained into it, only because it was used as a garbage dump, only because people threw in dead dogs and cats. Clean it out, bank it, fence it, said Ring, and it would be as pure as when the white men first found it. Furthermore, it would be a quick solution. "The above plan, if entered on with spirit, and briskly pursued, may be compleated by the beginning of July or of August next. . . ."

Even Dr. Joseph Browne, one of the backers of pure water from the Bronx River, conceded that the Collect, "after it has been renewed by a constant pumping for a few months, might be thought sufficiently pure for culinary purposes." It would at least do to wash and cool the streets and preserve the city from fire.

Obviously the people wanted water and they wanted it now. Accurately gauging the pulse of public opinion, Burr and the Manhattan Company negotiated for the site of Christopher Colles' old well and reservoir adjacent to Collect Pond, ordered thousands of feet of log pipe bored, and sent laborers into the principal streets to break up the pavement. When the log pipes were ready they were buried five feet down, two feet from the curb. For the first time, New York City, like any growing organism, had pushed roots down into the earth.

At first the city was elated. Within seven months the Manhattan Company announced that it was ready to serve customers! Pipes had been laid downtown along Broadway, with lateral mains reaching along the side streets toward the Hudson and East rivers. The company boasted that it was prepared to supply five thousand families with a daily supply of at least fifty gallons each "of a quality excellent for drinking and good for every culinary purpose."

Few noticed certain modest revisions in the company's original plan. There was no steam engine pumping water at Colles' old well, it was a spavined old horse instead. There was no million-gallon reservoir built down on Chambers Street either—it was only a tenth that size, though imposing enough to look at. The reservoir was built of flagstone, clay, sand and tar and wore a false front of four Doric columns supporting a recumbent figure of Oceanus. From the start the company's claims far exceeded its abilities. Only six miles of pipe were laid in the first year, supplying only four hundred homes. The water could not have been too wondrously fine-tasting either, since part of it was consumed while Miss Juliana Sands, a beautiful, but dead, young woman, was floating in the tank. No one ever explained how her corpse had got there, nor how long it had drifted about before being discovered.

The wooden pipes proved impractical too. The company was forever digging up the streets to repair or replace them, causing endless traffic jams. Foreign matter constantly became lodged in them, so that subscribers, turning their petcocks, got either a small trickle of water, or no water at all.

By 1803, one subscriber was angry enough to denounce the company in the popular press.

"Not long since [he wrote] I discharged my tea-water man and had a Manhattan cock introduced into my cellar, and for the first ten days I was highly pleased with it, as it afforded me good water— But, alas! for the last fourteen days, I have turned my cock repeatedly, but nothing comes from it—I have therefore been obliged to use the water which comes from the pump opposite the Marshall's door in Pearl Street."

The people of New York were not happy with the new water. it was, at up to $20 a year, expensive, and was supplied only to those who could afford it. This was far too dear for the poor, who went on as they had for more than a century, collecting rain water from their rooftops or buying an occasional pailful from fetid wells.

Nor was the city as a body satisfied, for normally there was not enough pressure in Manhattan Company pipes to control a healthy fire, and usually the engines had to be supplemented by bucket brigades reaching to the riverbanks. There were of course no hydrants; holes were merely drilled in the wooden pipes, which then spouted water like broken blood vessels. When the fire was finally out, and all bystanders had stolen a pail or two of "free" water, plugs were driven into the wounded pipe, stanching it. This, it is said, was the origin of the term "fireplug."

At its best, the Manhattan Company never laid more than twenty-five miles of mains, nor supplied more than two thousand homes—far under its original promise. From the beginning, the company had no heart for the job. The banking business was too profitable, the water business too much of a nuisance. From time to time the company tried to get out from under, to sell or lease its water rights to the city or to another company. Each time this either failed, or else the company backed off hurriedly, afraid that it might lose its banking privileges if it gave up its water. And so it continued for forty more years as a half-hearted water company; the cholera and yellow fever epidemics continued for forty more years too, and the all-consuming fires. Even after the company had finally given up the pretense of supplying water, and was firmly entrenched as one of the world's great banks, it maintained a few miles of pipes and its pumps kept its reservoir filled to a certain level, as required in the original charter—the only legal excuse for its continued existence.

Aaron Burr had done great mischief, and the city would go on paying for a long time, even though Burr himself never reaped profits. He was a brilliant politician. His long-range goal appears to have been to remake the New World in his own image. His was a dream of empire. He saw himself enthroned, wearing purple, molding the destiny of a continent. He was vain, amatory, ambitious, unprincipled.

In September, 1799, in a duel Burr took a shot at John B. Church, one of his associates on the Manhattan Company's board of directors and, although he missed Church, he appears to have shot himself out of a job. He was not a very nice person and his constituents saw this as soon as he had foisted the Manhattan Company upon them; the duel only confirmed it. They threw him out of the State Assembly, his associates dropped him from the board of directors of the Manhattan Company, and Hamilton cast the single vote which deprived him of the Presidency of the United States in 1801. When he killed Hamilton in a duel in 1804, Aaron Burr was ruined once and for all. He had hoped to parlay "pure and wholesome" water into making himself President, then emperor. No demagogue had ever used water as a weapon of conquest before, and Burr might have succeeded if his water had been of better quality. But the water which coursed through the wooden pipes was foul, and quenched the thirst of no man, least of all Aaron Burr.

3. The Great Water Celebration

THE PEOPLE OF NEW YORK showed their displeasure with the Manhattan Company by finding ways to use its water without paying for it. Subscribers would invite neighbors into their cellars to fill buckets and jugs with Manhattan water free of charge. The subscriber paid only a flat rate; what did he care how much Manhattan water he wasted or gave away? To heavy purchasers, grocers and other merchants gave away water as freely as they give green stamps today. Storekeepers near the water front permitted ship captains to fill their casks in return for business. All this was against the rules of the company, which cried out in pained indignation at such illegal practice. The people of New York either laughed or sneered, and went on doing it.

The company, by 1808, was making a profit of more than $10,000 a year on water alone, the water growing dirtier and nastier with every passing month.

The New York *Evening Post* attacked irately: "Some wells have been dug in the filthiest corners of the town; a small quantity of water has been conveyed in wretched wooden pipes, now almost worn out, for family use; and in a manner scarcely, if at all preferable to the former method of supplying water by the carts."

Some pipes became stopped up by poplar roots growing through them. Complained the *Commercial Advertiser:* "The

31

inhabitants of the southern part of our city have not had a pitcher of Manhattan water for the last five or six days. The extreme heat of the weather, and the parching drought which at present afflicts the city, have made this unaccountable deprivation doubly afflicting."

Once the company announced that service would be suspended for two weeks while a new steam-powered pump was installed. Two weeks lengthened into three, four. The public reacted with bitter letters to the newspapers:

"It is high time that there was some steps taken to compel the Manhattan Company to supply this city with good and wholesome water. . . . For five weeks we have received no water, and the collectors call and insult the inhabitants for not giving them the money for water which they do not receive. It is abominable indeed for the city to be thus trifled with and abused by the company."

It was during this period that the Manhattan Company tried to get out from under; then, fearing the loss of banking privileges, decided not to.

The population of New York City had swelled to 130,000 by 1822, when the city was again scourged by yellow fever. Persistent surveys had been made as to how, and from where, pure water might be brought in. Some schemes were smothered by the Manhattan Company itself; others died for lack of a dynamic personality to push them, though the need was evident: fifteen prominent physicians had signed certificates to the effect that Manhattan Company water was unfit for human consumption. One doctor warned that it "abounds in earthy and saline materials, highly injurious to the constitution, when so constantly taken into it by our daily beverage . . . frequently productive of diseases of the stomach and bowels, especially with strangers upon their first use of it. Gravel and other complaints of the kidneys are of frequent occurrence among our citizens, and I believe are oftentimes attributable to the water as their source."

The company, running scared, tried to appease the public by boasting of the pipes it was forced constantly to repair: "The quality of the water is as good as can be found; and the Company, having lately replaced many of the old pipes with new ones, the water will be received clearer and in better order than heretofore."

Fast-talking public relations men (though the phrase was not then in use) worked night and day trying to convince the city that Manhattan water was not as bad as it tasted. A carpet and dye manufacturer, identified in a company blurb as an "expert" in chemistry, wrote a pamphlet to the effect that the water did not contain poisonous chemicals resembling putty and white lead, as had been alleged. The water merely contained "small" amounts of lime and soda—which were not impure, just unpleasant-tasting.

Whereupon, to reassure the community, the "expert" mixed Manhattan water with copperas and oil and painted the door of his factory with it. What this demonstration was supposed to prove is not clear. Perhaps that the water was not strong enough to eat away the door.

The Manhattan Company, still panicky, next came up with an "expert" at drilling deep wells. Down, down, down some 442 feet into the earth bored this expert, but the water forced to the surface was no better than that already stagnating in company tanks.

Other individuals soon joined the deep-well kick. A tanner named Jacob Lorillard owned a swamp on Jacob Street. One day Lorillard and some cronies, sitting around a bottle of whisky, decided that the swamp must be fed by some deep underground stream. Drilling apparatus was forthwith brought in at great expense, and sure enough, 128 feet down, a vein of water was struck. Lorillard and his pals crowded around for a taste from the first full bucket brought to the surface, water which would make them all rich.

Lorillard sipped from the dipper and nearly choked. One by one the others had their turn. Some spat the water out, others gagged and nearly vomited. It was the worst-tasting water any of them had ever drunk.

"Ruined," gasped Lorillard. "We're ruined."

"That water," said another, "is as foul as any medicine."

Suddenly Lorillard was struck by an idea. "Wait a minute," he cried. "Maybe we can still get our money back. Maybe we can sell it as medicine."

And that is what these enterprising Yankees proceeded to do. The swamp was renamed "Jacob's Well," the beverage which burbled out of the bore was called mineral water, and its foul taste was advertised far and wide as being the instrument of all manner of marvelous cures. Jacob's Well water was said to relieve arthritis, rheumatism, dizziness and head colds, and was especially recommended for children, pregnant women and those with heart disease.

It did not, however, relieve the water shortage. A great deal of Jacob's Well water was sold in that year of our Lord 1827, and was duly forced down the throats of squalling children, or heroically swallowed by the ill and the faint. But the city soon caught on. Someone analyzed the water and found that the taste came from old boots and tan bark—the refuse of two centuries buried in the soil behind the tannery.

Perhaps even some of those who had been duped snickered at mankind's gullibility, after the news got out. But no one snickered when the shocking fire losses of 1828 were totaled, or when count was taken of the number of babies carried off that same year by one plague or another.

The city had to have water.

Lacking it, the city of course lacked sewers too. At this time only four stone sewers had been built, and they were intended to carry off storm water. The largest of them was the one under Canal Street, which also drained the pesky springs which had nourished the now filled-in Collect Pond.

Most houses were equipped with gutters made of wood, stone or brick, into which dish water and other kitchen slops were poured. The gutters ran into the back yard, emptying into homemade cesspools in some cases, or simply spilling out upon the ground in others.

When the cesspool became full, the enterprising home-owner usually built a second gutter which carried the overflow to the nearest stream. Thus all the streams which watered the island gradually became sewers.

The first stream to succumb still trickles on today, deep under Broad Street in the financial district. In places it is trapped into modern sewers, in others it escapes again. Not all the weight of the city will ever smother it completely.

Once this stream ran through old Nieuw Amsterdam, making Dutch settlers, who gazed upon it, more and more homesick for the canals of the Netherlands which they would never see again. Canals were a symbol of home to them, and they wanted one here in their new home in the New World. So they began to work at the stream, widening it, deepening it, straightening it. At last they had a canal of their own or, rather, a stream which to them looked like one.

Then Nieuw Amsterdam surrendered to the practical British who forthwith rooted out sentiment. In 1680 the Dutchmen's canal was roofed over by a roadway—it was already a sewer anyway, claimed the English. The new road, called Broad Street, became popular for promenades because of its canopy of shade trees. Broad Street is still shady today—it is as dark and narrow as a trench, in fact—but it is shaded not by trees but by brick and steel and money.

The sanitary habits of the city did not change much during the next century and a half. Refuse was heaped in all the streams in turn, and there were no more fishermen and picnickers about them at all.

Most families built privies in the yard behind their homes. There was also, beginning about 1650 and lasting almost two hundred years, a legion of "humble" men (actual slaves during one period) who, as the population increased and the land was used up, contracted to carry buckets of filth from the homes of the well-to-do to dump in the Hudson or East River.

There was no Department of Sanitation. Chickens and pigs cleaned the streets, into which householders were accustomed to empty "tubbs of odour and nastiness." It is said that the East Side, above Fiftieth Street, depended upon pigs until after the Civil War. Charles Dickens, among the early visitors, hated New York; he couldn't stand the perpetual rooting about and munching of the pigs. The city cleaned the streets once a week during the warm months, and not at all during the winter. Piles of ashes, garbage and other slop washed back into the cellars every time it rained.

Under these not-too-ideal conditions, plagues flourished.

The worst yellow fever epidemic occurred in 1805 when it was estimated that twenty-six thousand people (almost half the population) fled the city to escape it, trying to find refuge in tiny Greenwich Village to the north, or across the bay in the City of Brooklyn.

Yellow fever also decimated New York in 1795, 1798, 1819 and 1822. In 1832 and 1834, cholera paid terrifying visits.

The city had to have water.

Even in the midst of the horror and mystery of the cholera epidemics, the muddling about went on and on. Common Councils met, talked and dissolved. Mayors orated, citizens pleaded. Possible sources of "pure and wholesome" water were discussed, the Bronx River, the Croton River, Rye Pond, the Hudson River itself. Engineering survey after engineering survey was made, considered and forgotten. The city's brewers, a half-million-dollar industry, circulated a petition to the effect that they could no longer compete with beer from Philadelphia, unless they got better water. Tourists no longer came to New York. "Our water is very bad," noted one official. "Travellers all speak against it, and often therefore they will not reside in this city longer than they possibly can." Clergymen railed at the rise in drunkenness as men spiked Manhattan water with better-tasting stuff. People were back to buying water from the cartmen which, since it was carried around in the hot sun, was never cold enough to make a refreshing drink. A doctor who was also a part-time politician, revealed that impurities in the water came largely from graveyards and privies: "Into the sand bank underlying the city are daily deposited quantities of excrementitious matter, which were it not susceptible of demonstration would appear almost incredible. With our present population, there is put into this sand about 100 tons of excrement every 24 hours. In these deposits we may find all the ingredients detected by analysis, and which destroy the purity of our waters." The city was so dirty that it stank: "A person coming in the city from the pure air of the country, is compelled to hold his breath, or make use of some perfume to break off the disagreeable smell arising from the streets."

THE GREAT WATER CELEBRATION 37

Every year there seemed to be a new man with a new plan for bringing water to New York. Arising, he would strike down the man and plan which had come before him, and present his own theory, his own figures. There would follow a great deal of loud conversation and considerable publicity. Then he, too, would be struck down by an even newer man with an even newer plan—or perhaps the same plan urged several years back, which everyone, by now, had forgotten. It didn't matter, nothing happened. A few wells were drilled, a few million gallons of unpalatable water were pumped to the surface; a great iron reservoir was even built at Broadway and Fourteenth Street. It stood about ten stories high—higher than anything else in the city—and contained 233,000 gallons of brackish well water which was constrained to course under the streets through (for the first time) new iron pipes. It was hoped at first that iron pipes instead of wooden ones would improve the taste of the water. They didn't.

It seems incredible that such need could have existed for so long and nothing be done about it. In 1832 Asiatic cholera, a new and terrifying killer visited New York for the first time and slaughtered 3,500 people. The city did not need science to tell it that foul water and filthy streets helped spread the disease. Everyone seemed to know that.

Still nothing was done except that talk was added to talk. It was not a matter of money. The Manhattan Company was collecting $10,000 a year in water fees; the Tea-water men and other carters were earning about $275,000 selling water by the bucket; in the harbor, ship captains were paying over $50,000 a year to have their casks refilled before putting to sea; fire wiped out a quarter of a million dollars' worth of property a year; the 1832 cholera epidemic cost at least that much.

At those prices, it was estimated, New York could pay off a new aqueduct within five years!

There were, and always had been, many proponents of the aqueduct idea, but enough of them had never been able to decide on what type of aqueduct ought to tap which source. United, New Yorkers might have had water years before. Divided, they were never able to outshout the various profiteers and morons who infested the city, still insisting that well water would do the trick, that Manhattan water was not too bad, once you got used to it. One plan called for the drilling of forty-two wells in various corners of the city, each to be surmounted by a smoky, clattering steam engine to pump the water up. The Manhattan Company's "expert" well driller went into partnership with another schemer and the two of them commenced to prey upon public fear and grief following the cholera epidemic. They, and they alone, had the means of boring down to the pure, deep-running water which would keep the disease from killing *your* little girl, *your* small son.

Then all at once the aqueduct men seemed to settle it among themselves. The Croton River, forty miles north of the city, was the source to be tapped, a closed masonry aqueduct was the only sensible method. A great new reservoir would be built at Murray Hill (Forty-second Street and Fifth Avenue, now the site of the Public Library). The project would cost about $5,000,000, it would take more than six years to build. Let's get started.

With this agreement, opponents of the aqueduct plan were done for. Legal machinery worked noisily and none too confidently, but it did work. When the polls closed on April 16, 1835, the people of New York had ratified the Croton project by 17,330 votes to 5,963. Almost all the nays came from uptown districts where well water was not yet polluted.

Soon there would be water enough for all, water to ward off disease, water to drench fires. Soon, but not soon enough.

That winter fire started in the Comstock and Andrews Department Store in what is now the financial district and spread to neighboring buildings. All night it blazed on, and into the next day. There was not enough water to fight it and soon it was beyond all control. The Merchants' Exchange was consumed, and the Old Dutch Church and 674 other buildings and stores. Two thousand storekeepers were ruined, as were all the city's insurance companies. Ten thousand clerks and salesgirls were out of work. The city was in ashes.

Damage, for want of sufficient water, was estimated at perhaps twenty-five million dollars.

The construction of the Croton Dam and Aqueduct, now quickly begun, ran into snags. Westchester farmers refused to sell land which the dam would inundate; when it was made clear to them that they had to sell, want to or not, they fought a delaying action in the courts, and obstructed actual field work by whatever means they could. Surveying stakes mysteriously disappeared, tools were stolen and crews threatened with shotguns and accused of trespassing. Damage claims were frequent and outrageously high.

Most of the laborers were Irish immigrants, an easygoing lot anxious to patronize local taverns after work. Regulations were passed forbidding the sale of liquor to the workers, who numbered about three thousand, a very thirsty army. But the thirst of the Irish, and the chance for profit, caused woodland speakeasies to be set up where, according to a commission report, the "enemy of man may be obtained in any quantity for money." Frequent riots broke out, most of them strictly intramural, such as the 1838 battle between the men from Cork and those who had originated in Ferman. Bones were broken, including a few thick heads, and one man was killed.

Nevertheless, work proceeded steadily. Tunnels were bored, the five-mile-long dam near the mouth of the Croton River was put into place, and a massive arch bridge was erected to span a valley near Sing Sing. The major engineering problem was to bring the aqueduct across the Harlem River just above the present site of Yankee Stadium.

There were two plans for this, a high arched bridge which would soar majestically across from the heights on one side of the river to those on the other; or a completely uninteresting (but far cheaper) low bridge which would plod across the river just above the surface of the water. A low bridge would forever block the Harlem River to navigation by great ships.

Each plan had determinedly vocal adherents, and first one side, then the other, appeared to be leading. The Common Council, having met to arbitrate the point, was unable to come to a decision. The Chief Engineer, John B. Jervis, predicted in December, 1839, that the high bridge faction would ultimately win out. This pleased him. "As you know," he admitted, "engineers are prone to gratify a taste for the execution of prominent works."

This was too much for an *Evening Post* correspondent who wrote angrily: "This is the age of humbugs, but beyond controversy the high bridge will be the highest of all humbugs. For what purpose is it proposed to erect a stone bridge 1,450 feet in length, with an elevation of 163 feet above the rock at the bottom of the river, which rock on which the pier must rest is in places 32 feet below the surface of the water? Why this most stupendous and unparalleled bridge must be erected to secure from interruption the navigation of Harlem River—a river that has never been navigated since the creation!"

Others advocated lowering the height of the proposed bridge and widening it at least a little, so that it could support a roadbed. This plea was ignored; though it was entirely sensible, the wheels of civic decision were already in ponderous motion and could no longer be stalled. When constructed, the High Bridge was one of the world's greatest spans, but it was (and remains to this day) wide enough only for a footpath. Under the footpath were to run two cast-iron pipes three feet in diameter, specially constructed so that leakage from them could never injure the bridge.

The bridge itself was never popular with pedestrians. A long and lonely quarter-mile hike, it was too high, too narrow, too empty. The High Bridge was never like other bridges, alive with the clatter of traffic. Upon it there is no sound except the whistle of the wind and to cross it, especially at night, gives a very eerie feeling.

By the summer of 1842 the Croton Dam was finished, even though it had had to be hastily rebuilt after a flash flood the year before had swept part of it away, drowning three persons and destroying much property. The thirty-three-mile aqueduct was completed between the dam and the Harlem River; the High Bridge would not be ready for another six years, but temporary pipes had been thrown across the river, connecting the aqueduct and the new Yorkville Reservoir, which in turn was connected to the new Murray Hill Reservoir at Forty-second Street. Below this last reservoir, some 165 miles of pipes had been laid under the streets of lower Manhattan.

All was in readiness at last. The people of New York waited

anxiously for their first taste of Croton water, for the day which would end the thirst of two centuries.

At last the great moment arrived. At dawn on June 22, 1842, atop the Croton Dam, a valve was thrown and water from the Croton River began to spill into the aqueduct. A little later a small boat named the *Croton Maid* was launched on the swelling current of the borning new river; four men clambered aboard. They were as alert and excited as explorers starting the perilous exploration of some new, uncharted waterway.

At the Harlem River end, a crowd began the long watch. All day people waited, having no idea how long it would take for the water to reach them. The night passed more slowly. Then all at once they became conscious of a new sound, the muted heavy movement of the oncoming water. Twenty-two hours had passed; it was three o'clock in the morning and they peered eagerly into the darkness. Yes, yes, there it was, Croton water! Now it surged toward them and a mighty cheer went up which lasted until the flood of water drowned it out.

Not far behind the crest rode the doughty *Croton Maid*, its crew tired but happy after their great adventure. The boat was successfully moored, and the four heroes climbed out.

Four days later the *Croton Maid* was portaged across the Harlem and put into the aqueduct again, having bypassed the temporary pipes which substituted for the unfinished High Bridge. Great pressure had now built up in the line above the Yorkville reservoir, every dignitary in town had had time to get to its banks, and multitudes of citizens were in their places. As soon as the sluice gates were opened, water gushed into the virgin reservoir, to be greeted by the thunderous salute of thirty-eight artillery pieces and enthusiastic applause. Just behind the crest of the water rode the *Croton Maid*—proof forever more that a *navigable* river had entered New York to assuage the thirst of its inhabitants.

By the Fourth of July the water had reached the Murray Hill Reservoir, and was immediately channeled into the tanks at Thirteenth Street for fire protection. The tanks were almost dry. If a fire had started a day or two before . . .

The big celebration was scheduled for October 14, and big

it was. Water seemed to have overpowered the city. Wrote one observer: "Nothing is talked of or thought of in New York but Croton water; fountains, aqueducts, hydrants, and hose attract our attention and impede our progress through the streets. Political spouting has given place to water spouts, and the free current of water has diverted the attention of the people from the . . . confused state of the national currency."

Church bells rang all day long. The explosion of a hundred cannon signaled the start of a parade which eventually attained a length of more than five miles, including regiments of soldiers, fifty-two companies of firemen, the city's butchers on horseback, and whole troops of marching temperance societies.

Those citizens who were not marching in the parade were jammed along the sidewalks or in windows watching it. Everyone appeared to be completely happy, overjoyed even, and one witness insisted that there were not even any drunks—so complete was the homage being paid to plain ordinary water!

All over town fountains bombarded the sky with jets and sprays and spouts of water. The water caught and reflected the glint of the sun. All the colors of the gayly bedecked city shone and glittered in it. To citizens the fountains seemed the most marvelous sight of all. Not only did New York finally have pure water, it had all it needed. It had even enough to waste.

In Union Square a fountain threw up "a noble column of water to a height as great almost as the houses that surround the square. . . . In the evening by the moonlight, the effect of the fountain showering its spray on every side, was exceedingly fine."

From a fountain in City Hall Park water gushed fifty feet high, above a basin a hundred feet in diameter, surmounted by "one main center jet and twenty-four subordinates, all of which can be changed to present different views and forms."

The parade lasted until five in the afternoon, when speeches began in City Hall Park. The Mayor spoke, the Governor spoke, the water commissioners spoke, everybody who was anybody spoke, and speechmaking began to seem even more interminable than the parade. No one complained, however.

It was all part of the pageant, of the greatest civic celebration the city had yet known. Odes written specially for the occasion were read and wildly applauded. Bands played. The merry-making went on and on.

Of course there was the inevitable grouch. One observer considered the delight of the common man to be somewhat gauche, and forthwith inscribed his own sophisticated reaction to Croton water. It was, he declared, "all full of tadpoles and animalculae," and flowed through an aqueduct which had been "used as a necessary by all the Hibernian vagabonds who worked upon it." This chap also jotted down the reaction of a friend, who was "in dreadful apprehension of breeding bull-frogs inwardly."

But most chroniclers of the day simply could not get enough of the new water.

"From the central channel-way in the streets [wrote one] the water finds its way readily into the houses right and left, where from cellar to attic, it is at all seasons and all hours instantly obedient to call. It needs but to turn the faucet when, presto! its sparkling drops rush forth in inexhaustible supplies. So willing, indeed, are the merry waters, and so much of their old mountain mischief do they still preserve, that without a care they may play you a melancholy prank or two, and, escaping through an unguarded vent, may disport themselves over your carpeted floors as among their native rocks and sands. . . ."

Another wrote: "I've led rather an amphibious life for the last week—paddling in the bathing tub every night and constantly making new discoveries in the art and mystery of ablution. Taking a shower bath upside down is the latest novelty. A real luxury, that bathing apparatus is. . . ."

On May 30, 1848, water was finally admitted into the pipes crossing the High Bridge, and a few weeks later the Croton Aqueduct was at last finished. Probably people had got used to the water by then, but it would be a generation or two before New York became blasé about it—too many people still remembered the taste of the water which Aaron Burr and the Manhattan Company had sent coursing through the slim wooden pipes.

Most persons were still proud and happy, like the man who wrote in his diary: "Rode to the High Bridge today. . . . Very great piece of work is the bridge, and very great city is this with all its absurdities."

4. Tunneling Through Bedrock

UNDER THE STREETS of New York, the iron mains fed by Croton water reached ever outward, like fingers groping for the extremities of the island. Water was such a novelty that people turned on their faucets just to watch it run. The city finally had enough hydrants to combat any fire—but unhappily they were too easy to turn on. Any youngster with a pair of pliers could do it, sending a jet of water across to the opposite curb and dousing anyone passing by. This became great sport. Gangs of small boys paraded through the city, searching for hydrants unguarded by beat-walking policemen. With a shriek and a holler, on would go the water, the boys howling with laughter as they sped away. Gallons of water, meanwhile, cascaded down the nearest sewer.

Water was wasted in other ways too, in the newfangled water closets (people loved the sound of flushing toilets), in the new public baths which had been erected (one large common bath for males, one for females, the price three cents; private tubs upstairs costing six cents) and in many other ways too. It was normal in winter, for instance, to leave the taps running all night. Otherwise, people feared, the pipes would freeze. And lastly there was the ever-expanding network of mains in the streets. By 1854, twelve years after the Croton water had come in, pressure was so low that water would not rise above the second story of buildings. There were no more majestic columns of water tilted by the wind above the fountains. The basins now were dry and barren.

Stopgap measures were employed to add more water. The Yorkville Reservoir, considered shallow, had its rock bottom dredged out. The two 36-inch pipes atop the High Bridge were supplanted by one 90-inch pipe. A new reservoir was built in Central Park.

The Croton Aqueduct, built to handle seventy-five million gallons a day, was now carrying twenty million more than that, but still the city was thirsty and by now, in steaming, over-crowded tenements water would mount one story only, no farther.

The aqueduct was so full that water spurted from the seams under its roof. The real villain was the pipes under the street —there were far more of them than the Croton engineers had ever anticipated.

So a new Croton aqueduct was built, running alongside the old one. Still there was no surplus water, as immigration swelled the population year by year and, in 1898, consolidation of the five boroughs doubled it in one fell swoop.

Heroic measures were called for and now, as the century turned, New York proved equal to the demand. New dams were built in the Catskill Mountains, ninety miles to the northwest of the city. A pressure tunnel through bedrock 1,114 feet down carried the water *under* the Hudson.

In Yonkers, at the northern outskirts of the city, Catskill water paused momentarily at the new Hill View Reservoir, then plunged into City Water Tunnel No. 1. Deep through bedrock, so far beneath the streets that not even an earthquake could reach it, it coursed through the tunnel toward Brooklyn, a vast underground river bringing a billion and a half gallons a day into the parched city.

This tunnel was, and remains, man's deepest penetration of the island.

At its construction (it was put into service in 1917) it was termed an engineering marvel equal to the Panama Canal. The years have served only to bear out this contention. Masonry bridges such as the old High Bridge might have been more picturesque; great iron pipes buried a few inches under the earth would certainly have been cheaper and quicker. But for sheer dependability and indestructibility, nothing else

All Manhattan Island is underlined with rock.

could have matched Tunnel No. 1 or No. 2 (which was finished in 1936). They will endure as long as the island endures.

In engineering parlance they are termed "pressure tunnels," meaning that water enters them under such pressure that ordinary pipes, even concrete reinforced pipes, would burst from the strain. The object was to bore the tunnels through solid bedrock so far down that the weight of the rock would equalize the pressure of the water.

In many parts of Manhattan, bedrock lies just under the sod. But the tunnels had to go much deeper, down where the rock was sound, no fissures, no decayed patches. To find rock hard enough and deep enough to serve, soundings were taken with diamond drills. Pipes an inch and a half in diameter were forced into the soil until they encountered bedrock. The drills were then inserted inside the pipes and boring begun. Each drillhead held six black diamonds, the diamonds alone being worth about $100 each (in 1905).

Down bored the drills, exactly as an auger bores through wood. And, in just the same way, shavings of rock collected on the drills' flanges. From time to time the drills would be withdrawn, the shavings of rock picked off and carefully labeled according to depth. In this way engineers were able to determine the quality, hardness and thickness of each strata of rock they bored through. In some places earth-filled, pre-glacial gorges in the bedrock were found, or geological faults where the rock was crushed or deeply decayed. In these spots the tunnel would have to go down, down ever deeper until sound rock was located which could resist the force and weight of the gushing river which would one day flow through it.

Section after section was added to the probing fingers of the drills. At last engineers had the information they needed. City Tunnel No. 1 would be bored through at depths of from 200 to 750 feet below street level. The circular tunnel, lined smooth with a foot or more thickness of concrete, would diminish from a diameter of fifteen feet in the Bronx and upper Manhattan, to eleven feet in Brooklyn. Imagining it as a street one could walk through, the tunnel would be full of steep inclines, some of them precipitous even, as it constantly sought the level of sound rock.

It was early determined to bore the tunnel under city property—streets and parks. That way there would be no arguments about, or payment demanded for right of way. The city's lawyers were not sure that a landowner could collect for a tunnel bored several hundred feet under his house, but it was better not to take the chance.

Besides, great gaping shafts had to be sunk down to the level where the tunnel boring would begin. There had to be elevators to send down men and equipment and, in places, pumps to send down water and air. All this, it was judged, would seem messy in a man's back yard.

And so twenty-five shafts were dug, four of them in Central Park, others in Van Cortlandt Park, Bryant Park, Jerome Park, Morningside Park, Fort Greene Park, and even amid the foliage of Madison Square and Cooper Square. In fact, wherever there are three or more trees standing together in this city, you can feel pretty sure there is a water tunnel somewhere underneath.

As men and gear moved in, park lovers of the day were outraged. So were derelicts accustomed to sleeping in these normally peaceful places. Indignant letters appeared regularly in the press. This or that monument which had graced the park for a century was actually *teetering*. This or that great tree which had given shade to Dutch settlers, had been split almost in two and was not expected to survive. And wasn't it awful that the city's parks could be treated in this way? Often the resignation of the Commissioner of Parks was demanded, because obviously he wasn't doing his job: Why didn't he make them put their dreadful tunnel some place else?

The biggest protest of all rose in 1916 when it was determined that a pumping station would have to be built above the shaft in Morningside Park.

No, No, No! cried park lovers and derelicts alike. But the wheels of progress crunched inexorably on, grinding protestations under foot. The harassed Park Commissioner even decided to join the attack, at least when speaking publicly. Plans of the soon-to-be-built pump house were produced by the Board of Water supply. It would have classical lines, the board promised; it would look Roman or Greek, it would enhance the beauty of the park.

"You call that classical?" snorted shade and flower lovers, when the architect's drawings were shown about. "It looks like a tomb!"

Taking a different tack, the board tried to woo the public by promising that the east and west wings of the proposed pump house would contain "comfort stations" [a euphemism used by the New York Park Department for public toilets] "of which Morningside Park has long had need."

"We have all the comfort stations we need," responded the opposition sullenly.

In the press, the case of the tomb-like pumping station smoldered many months and was not supplanted in public interest until the United States entered World War I the following year.

Meanwhile, work continued in the bowels of the city. Begun in 1907 with men boring toward each other from all twenty-five of the access shafts, the tunnel was at last linked together in January, 1914. This happened twice, once actually and once ceremonially.

At 7:00 AM, January 11, in the quiet residential district at St. Nicholas Avenue and 150th Street, half-awake men were drinking breakfast coffee prepared by cheerless wives. Suddenly the floor trembled, dishes rattled in the closet and probably a good deal of coffee spilled over into saucers.

Many must have looked up sharply, their faces frightened. But it was no earthquake. It was just the final holing through of the great water tunnel, 450 feet beneath the street.

The morning was still dark and bitterly cold when the cartridge men had descended into the tunnel to place their charges. A few minutes before seven the alarm had been sounded; from both sides of the last rock barrier, men backed off, crouching behind mine cars and other material. It was precisely seven o'clock when the electrician threw his switch. There was a thunderous explosion; for fully five minutes the ears of the men rang with its echo, and with the noise of shattered rock slowly subsiding into place. When the men went forward a shoulder of solid rock still blocked the lower portion of the tunnel, but there was an opening big enough for a man to crawl through above. The debris was swept back and the men began to call to their fellows on the other side of the divide. In a moment the tunnel rang with a new sound, with laughter and cheers. Across the shoulder of rock men reached out to shake hands with those who had been tunneling toward them all these months.

A little later, cases of beer were lowered into the tunnel and work halted for the day. The workmen commenced to get royally drunk, 450 feet below staid St. Nicholas Avenue. In a while they began making speeches, recounting the problems they had surmounted, the hardships endured, the epic contribution they were making to the city. There were speeches by foremen, then by ordinary laborers, and many of the speeches were in Italian. Because, just as Irish immigrants had built the Croton Aqueduct, so the current crop of immigrants had built the new Catskill Aqueduct—and the current crop happened to be Italian.

The speeches went on for an hour, getting progressively funnier as the beer supply diminished. It was as if these men were children, mimicking their elders who were expected at any moment.

For speechmaking in that tunnel was by no means at an end. Two days later, down into the tunnel marched Mayor John Purroy Mitchel, ex-Mayor George McClellan, Chief Engineer J. Waldo Smith and Charles Strauss, Chairman of the Board of Water Supply.

This time the men stood by, docile and a little bewildered, as persons whose profession it was to make speeches, took their turn. The ceremony, if it can be called that in the tight little corridor which had been bored through bedrock, was long and dull. What seems significant, looking back, is the incredible determination of these politicians (like politicians everywhere) to talk, no matter what the circumstances. For the speeches— because of the tons of rock and earth overhead, because of the impossible acoustics of the tunnel, because of the language problems of the only audience available—not only could not be heard aboveground, they were not even intelligible in the tunnel itself.

They were, nonetheless, made, while the workmen scuffed their feet idly, and some of them doubtless laughed inwardly, remembering the hilarious orations which had been made on that same spot only two days before.

At last all the dignitaries had had their say. The Mayor surveyed the barrier which had been stuffed with stones so as to seem formidable and thus heighten the drama of the occasion. Then the gentry hiked back three blocks for safety, and the Mayor threw the switch. This repeated the thunderous echoing roar of forty-eight hours ago, the concussion of air shot back past the knot of men with considerable force, and soon all were coughing on the dust.

Then they walked forward. Where the barrier had been there was now a great hole, through which shone a brightly shining star formed of Christmas tree bulbs.

A few minutes later, the Mayor and his band mounted an electric mine car to ride back to the shaft which would return them to the street. In climbing aboard, the Mayor's tall hat struck the trolley wire; sparks flew and a worker shouted that the Mayor had nearly electrocuted himself.

J. Purroy Mitchel, Mayor, was a considerably shaken man when he finally reached the cold, blowy morning aboveground. There he partially regained his composure and managed a smile at the barbershop quartette of tunnel workers who waited and who honored him and Engineer Waldo Smith with this song:

> "Wait till the dam is finished
> And the water is rising high
> We will be happy Waldo
> You and I.
> Down the aqueduct we'll wander
> John Purroy you and I
> If you will wait till the dam is finished
> By and by."

The tune was the familiar "Wait Till the Sun Shines, Nellie."

It was now possible for a man to walk underground from the Flatbush section of Brooklyn, all the way to the Catskill

Mountains, a distance of about 120 miles—provided anyone was balmy enough to want to.

Were there any such persons? There certainly were. Within a week nine had been discovered, seven of them reporters, two photographers. An expedition was quickly organized and announced in the papers. At dawn on January 18, 1914, this small knot of intrepid adventurers, complete with gear, notebooks and cameras, arrived at the Ashokan Dam in the Catskills, ready to begin the epic hike.

Also on hand was a large and derisive body of men who had worked on the aqueduct and knew it well. At the reporters and photographers they laughed and hooted and jeered.

"Had much mountain-climbing experience?"

"Don't ferget to rope yerselves together."

"The view don't change much in there."

"Hope none of yez gets lost."

The expedition's "Swiss" guide was an aqueduct engineer who was frankly dubious about chances of success.

"There are some subterranean Alpine climbs and descents in there," he warned.

The journalists, now patently uneasy, were obliged to go ahead with it—they had, unfortunately, bragged in print of their trek.

Goal for the first night was set at thirteen miles, at which point the group would be lifted out of a shaft in an elevator and would spend the night in warmer quarters, before re-entering the tunnel the next day.

But as the men entered the first shaft, leaving daylight behind them, the assembled, jeering workers were making bets on how far they'd get. Most decided that they would have had enough after about ten miles. (At that point the tunnel makes a sharp dip of eight hundred feet to pass under Rondout Creek.) All agreed that none would ever reach the other side of the Hudson.

As it happened, the journalists did actually make it to their scheduled first-night stopping point—but they hiked most of the distance aboveground, complaining that the tunnel was full of water. Whether it was or not is a moot point. The excuse of very weary and slightly scared men was backed up by Engineer Waldo Smith and served admirably to save face all around.

The next day the hike was formally abandoned.

There was still a great deal of work to do. The tunnel had to be enlarged and caked smooth as a tube with concrete—a tube fifteen feet in diameter. After that the access shafts had to be equipped with riser pipes and vales to bring the water up to the street mains and so into the homes of the city. The valves would be of bronze for permanence and would themselves be located a hundred or more feet down for safety. From the point where the tunnel ended in Brooklyn, steel pipes had to be laid through the streets to remote neighborhoods and a cast-iron siphon had to be entrenched in the floor of New York Bay across to Staten Island. When this work was finished the shaft sites would have to be cleaned up, regraded and resodded, and the huge spoil banks of rock which had been gouged out of the tunnel would have to be graded to lines fitting the adjacent topography, covered with earth and sodded. In the parks the shacks had to be torn down, damaged trees removed and new ones planted.

Meanwhile, in the Catskill watershed, other massive dams had to be fitted into place, dams which would soon trap enough water from mountain rivers and brooks to cover all of Manhattan Island to a depth of thirty feet. The water gushing through City Tunnel No. 1 would, were it flowing down Fifth Avenue at comfortable walking speed, reach from wall to wall at armpit level.

All types of workers were employed in building the new aqueduct, including gravediggers. Some thirty-two cemeteries were to be inundated, so the 2,800 bodies they contained all had to be exhumed and re-interred—"reverently" according to the board of water supply—elsewhere.

Seven villages, having a total permanent population of two thousand, also were relocated, as well as eleven miles of railroads and sixty-four miles of highway.

The aqueduct also caused the formation of a special police

force (Board of Water Supply Police) which, at the peak of construction in 1913, numbered 377 men and 300 horses. Operating out of twenty-four precincts, these "Mounties" patrolled the length of the aqueduct and were responsible for the prevention of everything from murders to immigrant laborers relieving themselves in the bushes of what would one day be the basin of New York's water.

Labor camps had been established along the route, some of them housing more than a thousand men and their families in temporary barracks-type buildings. All of the camps were as complete as army posts, including chapels, YMCAs, commissaries and social clubs, and it was the duty of the police force to keep fugitives from New York justice, all types of weapons, and whisky from mingling with the laborers.

Sanitation was a real problem. No matter how often they were preached to, the laborers could see no point in hiking back to this or that fancy toilet, when there was a good bush handy.

There was apparently only one occasion on which the Water Supply police were obliged to enter the tunnel in line of duty. The New York *Times* described the scene thus:

"A riot was started in an excavation 1,200 feet below the earth's surface. The workers were attacking one another with picks and shovels. It looked as though much blood would be shed. A signal of distress was telephoned from below. . . . The police were lowered into the excavation in a bucket. As they neared the bottom of the hole the din from clashing spades and picks and cries of anger and distress were terrific. The police with drawn revolvers waded into the thickest of the fray, where they laid low several of the ringleaders with their long nightsticks. Although outnumbered 20 to 1, they by their courage brought what looked like a mortal fight to a speedy termination."

The article concluded that the principal requisites of an aqueduct policeman (who earned $1,050 a year) were "courage and physical health."

By October 12, 1917, the Catskill Aqueduct was finished and a great crowd assembled in Central Park for the celebration. Musical exercises were scheduled, as well as an allegorical pageant written specially for the occasion called "The Good Gift of Water." More than 15,000 school children had been obliged (despite the Columbus Day holiday) to attend, and they fretted and squirmed as the Mayor launched into his speech.

Whereupon the clouds opened and rain poured down. The Mayor hesitated, turned up his coat collar, then ran for cover. Most of the kids, unexpectedly delivered from what is, to children, a fate worse than death, were so delighted they just stood there in the rain. There would be no allegorical pageant now. The day had suddenly become a holiday again.

At the 1917 celebration a fountain in the park sent a column of water eighty feet high. It was as if the city were flaunting its new luxury in the face of heaven. It's true that Croton water proved insufficient to our needs, the fountain seemed to say. But Catskill water, flowing through the deep tunnel, will last forever.

This insolence persisted a few weeks only. New reservoirs were planned and built, because experts already saw that the city was getting thirsty again. City Tunnel No. 2 was conceived in 1924 and built between 1929 and 1936. Like its brother, it was bored through bedrock at an average depth of five hundred feet. It is slightly longer (twenty miles) and slightly larger (seventeen feet in diameter). Proceeding south from the Hill View Reservoir in Yonkers, it crosses the East Bronx, passes under Rikers Island, through Queens and into Brooklyn. It does not touch Manhattan.

Because the lowest reservoir in the Catskill Aqueduct is 280 feet above sea level (the height of a twenty-eight-story building) and because there is a great weight of water behind the dams, water will gush through the tunnels into the city and shoot to the twenty-eighth story of buildings without pumping. In fact, Croton water, which reaches the city under much less pressure, is sent into the tunnels and bred with this pressure, instead of being pumped as formerly.

Perhaps this matter of pressure does not sound important, but it saves the city a great deal of money and indicates graphically the consummate artistry with which the city tunnels and the entire Catskill Aqueduct were built.

5. Subways or Els

As LATE AS 1864, as the Civil War ground to a close, civilization weighted only the lower third of Manhattan Island. The cluster of wooden and brick structures, with a few six-story "skyscrapers" south of Twenty-third Street, made up the city's business district, the sedate residential area of its well-to-do, its slums. More than seven hundred thousand people were jammed into teeming, compact New York. (More arrived every day as immigrants and refugees.) The suburbs straggled only as far north as Forty-second Street.

Today Forty-second Street is one of the world's brightest, busiest thoroughfares. There, massed between the U.N. Building on the East River and the transatlantic piers of the Hudson, rise mighty office buildings, hotels and department stores, the bulky Public Library and squat Grand Central Terminal. The great spike of the 77-story Chrysler Building seems to pierce the sky. Six subway lines crisscross underneath. In one two-block area the marquees of seventeen movie houses blaze all night long.

But in 1864 Forty-second Street crossed the narrow island like a frontier. Few paved streets ran any farther. Beyond rose rocky eminences crowned with squatters' shanties, and beyond that deer jumped fences to graze in what was then called The Central Park. Madison Avenue was still being graded and the world had never heard of the "hard sell." Harlem had been discovered, but few went there. The occasional farms of northern Manhattan were bordered by forests, by clear, cool ponds and fast streams.

The Hudson River Railroad, the New York and Harlem, and the New Haven Railroad all touched the city limits, and a man could ride to Albany, 150 miles away, in only a day.

But there was, in effect, no transportation inside the city itself. New York was suffocating. The rivers and tenements pressed in on three sides. Expansion was possible only northward—if a means could be found to get there conveniently.

Public ox-carts had plodded up Broadway to Houston Street as early as 1746. Progress was slow. Forty years passed before the first horse-drawn cab appeared. In 1800 whips cracked over teams of horses and people rode in elongated stage coaches. Fares were twelve and a half cents below Fourteenth Street, eighteen and three quarters to Yorkville, and twenty-five cents for the long journey to Harlem.

Then, in 1832 tracks glistened in sudden sunlight along Fourth Avenue as horse-drawn street cars were introduced. People slogged through mud or dust to reach them in the center of the streets.

By 1864 there were a dozen such lines and sixty-one million passengers a year. Stages, called omnibuses, sometimes ran as frequently as every thirteen seconds—at a busy corner like Chambers Street, 230 to 240 would pass in an hour.

Competition between rival stagecoach companies, and between stages and streetcars, was violent, often cutthroat. No tracks hampered the operations of the stages, whose drivers ran over men, women and children in their haste to beat competitors to waiting passengers. Burly conductors shanghaied people into coaches and forced them to pay, so that heavy profits could be shown. Drivers were picked for heft, not courtesy. Most swore at the passengers, and swindled them on tickets and on change. Axles broke, horses shied and policemen on boxes at intersections spent more time separating slugging rival drivers than directing snarled traffic. Clergymen in white chokers were shocked, women disgusted, children wept. "Modern martyrdom," wrote the New York *Herald* of October 2, 1862, "may be succinctly defined as riding in a New York omnibus."

The streetcars were quieter, but much more crowded. People were packed in as tightly as in today's subways—but those were less callous times, and such overcrowding was considered insupportable. Silks and broadcloths were ruined in attempts to enter or exit. Pocketbooks, watches and breastpins vanished via pickpockets. The air was poisonous and it was said that a healthy person could not ride a dozen blocks without a headache. Ladies and gentlemen preferred the stages, whose fare was ten cents. The streetcars cost only six. The common people could not afford more.

And so in 1864 it began to be whispered about that only a subway could save the city. Even as engineers, scientists and visionaries cast about for a practical method, a Michigan railroad man, Hugh B. Willson, organized the Metropolitan Railway Company, attracted prominent backers and raised $5,000,-000 for a subway. One of those who did not approve of plans to tunnel Manhattan was railroad magnate Cornelius Vanderbilt. Snorted the Commodore: "I'll be underground a damned sight sooner than this thing."

Willson's engineer, A. P. Robinson, proposed glass sidewalks over stations to eliminate daytime lighting problems, hollow lampposts every hundred feet to funnel down fresh air, and steam engines burning coke to reduce smoke in the tunnel. Trains, receiving a telegraphic signal from the central starter, would start at exactly the same moment from stations exactly half a mile apart. Thus there would be no trains in between, and each driver had only to reach the next station in the allotted ninety seconds. If the train did not show up on time, the "platform superintendent" would signal the starter to hold everything. For safety's sake, Robinson suggested, each platform superintendent might even be enabled to switch out the starting system completely.

All this sounds naïve and haphazard today, but it was a scheme with much merit. Details had been carefully worked out, including the rearrangement of sewerage and water pipes, tunneling procedures, and the amount of passengers and revenue which might be realized. "The end of mud and dust, of delays due to snow and ice," crowed Robinson. "The end of the hazardous walk into the middle of the street to board the car, the end of waiting for lazy or obstinate truckmen. Everything will be out of sight, out of hearing. Nothing will indicate the great thoroughfare below."

Willson took the plans, the names of his backers and evidence of the $5,000,000, before the New York State Legislature toward the close of the 1864 session. When the bill failed to pass, Willson was calm. The legislators were merely in a hurry to get home, he reasoned. Reintroduced the following spring, the bill passed the Assembly by eighty-nine votes, greater than Willson's wildest expectations. New York's first subway must have seemed tantalizingly close that night. Willson, a quiet, earnest man who yearned for the kind of immortality the subway could give him, celebrated his victory with a glass of champagne.

Governor Ruben E. Fenton promptly vetoed the bill.

The New York *Times* hinted darkly: "We think this action will be regretted by all citizens except those who are interested in existing or anticipated street railroads." The insinuation was clear. A bluff and hearty politician named William Marcy "Boss" Tweed controlled the city. The streetcar and stage companies were in his pocket. So was the Governor.

There were no provisions for speedy completion of the work, Governor Fenton had argued. Due to accident, or lack of money, construction might drag on and on, the streets ripped up and traffic halted.

Willson, worried now, sought agreement on a waiver which would enable the bill to pass and work to start. Fenton again refused.

Willson was a good man, but an amateur at politics, and it appears that he never knew what he was up against. A flood of bills now were introduced, some by opponents of the subway merely to confuse the issue, others by unscrupulous men who saw the value of Willson's ideas, but meant to have his profits for themselves.

Willson, bewildered, finally decided to resubmit his bill without changes, requesting respectfully that the Legislature tack on such amendments as it thought necessary.

But his opponents, notably Origen Vandenburgh and Jacob Sharpe, had brought up heavy guns and Willson was under fire from all sides. Timid old men spoke of fear of catching cold due to entering Willson's tunnel on a hot day. Health experts testified that engine smoke in the tunnel would be injurious to human life. And as a trump card, A. W. Craven, Chief Engineer of the Croton Reservoir, was induced to declare that Willson's subway would disrupt sewerage facilities and cause water pressure to lapse in downtown New York. Only a few months before, Craven had been in favor of the subway.

Willson listened in a dazed, unbelieving silence as his dream was torn down around him. "This is a bold act of piracy," he cried desperately at one point. When at last he rose to speak, it was too late. He looked down at the faces of the Legislature and knew that he was beaten.

That defeat crushed Willson. His friends made a feeble effort in his behalf the following year. But there were two other bills, one of them Vandenburgh's, and the perplexed senators could not decide between them. Vandenburgh was one of the most accomplished lobbyists of his time. His intentions (were they merely to sabotage Willson, or to advance a subway of his own?) remained murky to the end, as did his conduct. As the session closed, Senator Lebau charged that $10,000 had been paid certain senators to vote for Vandenburgh's bill. The charge was never proved.

As for Willson, he probably would have failed even if his bill had passed. For Boss Tweed had not yet entered the skirmish openly. Tweed, intent on exacting tribute from all sides, was determined that there should be no change in existing public transportation. And Tweed, in 1867, was Emperor of New York.

Those were busy times for Tweed. The year before, Charles Harvey, an inventor, had proposed an elevated railway along Ninth Avenue, perhaps as far north as Yonkers. A superstructure carrying the tracks would be erected on either side of the street at the sidewalk line. Stationary engines, anchored to bedrock every fifteen hundred feet, would yank the trains along by reeling in cable.

Possibly because this scheme sounded silly, possibly because he considered subways to be the real threat to his iron grip on

New York, Tweed did not oppose Harvey at Albany. The bill slipped past the Legislature in 1866. Harvey, his little company self-consciously calling itself The Wst Side and Yonkers Patent Railway, then erected a single experimental track along Greenwich Street.

On July 1, 1868, a jeering multitude assembled to watch the public testing of Harvey's contraption. He would kill himself, the mob predicted. The El would collapse of its own weight.

Harvey himself, wearing a frock coat, flowing whiskers and a new stovepipe hat, climbed aboard the dinky little car to "risk his life," for the Ninth Avenue El.

"How The Old Thing Works," headlined the *Herald* next day. "Boiler Found Liable to Burst!"

After a cautious run down the track, Harvey had opened the throttle wide. Furiously, noisily, the engine wound in cable, and Harvey raced along at ten miles an hour!

The demonstration won him official approval, and now at last he was able to mortgage the line to reputable banks. Harvey and his friends had raised $100,000 to start work. It was not enough and he had been begging from usurious lenders for weeks.

The establishment of credit proved a mixed blessing to Charles Harvey. Pillar by pillar, rail by rail, the Ninth Avenue El crept toward the Hudson River Railroad Terminal at Thirtieth Street, the point where it could reasonably expect to begin making money. It was only twenty blocks away on September 26, 1869, Black Friday, start of the great depression.

Harvey was broke, and when some fast businessmen from Wall Street moved in on him, he was more grateful than wise. Soon this syndicate had control, and Harvey was blandly informed that he was a figurehead. The new plan was to discredit the El until all stock could be bought cheaply. The line would then be completed to Thirtieth Street, the stock would boom, would be resold, and all would enjoy fancy profits.

"You can't do that," protested Harvey. "It's dishonest."

Harvey was forced out of the company.

On November 15, 1870, the completed portion of the track,

six car bodies and three passenger cars, were sold at sheriff's sale.

Now Boss Tweed re-entered. The Tammany leader had laughed at the El at first, but he was laughing no longer. The thing threatened to bestride the city. Tweed had smothered the subway. But New York was desperate for rapid transit. Tweed felt that, if the El were ever permitted to reach Grand Central Terminal, it was certain to succeed.

So he promptly decided to get rid of it.

State Senator William Marcy Tweed forced a bill through the New York State Senate which branded the El a public nuisance, and which authorized the Commissioner of Public Works, also William Marcy Tweed, to tear it down within ninety days.

The vote counted, Boss Tweed laughed.

"You've given me ninety days," he boasted. "It will only take me sixty!"

The bill was sent to the Assembly. The Governor had received instructions from Tweed and was waiting to sign it, the moment the Assembly sent it on.

Harvey was powerless. There was no time even to seek an injunction. It was not his El any longer, but he did not care about that. The El was the supreme work of his life and he could not bear to see it casually, willfully destroyed, though he never earned a penny from it. He appealed to his friend, Erastus Corning, to plead for it before the Assembly.

Many years before, Harvey had saved Corning's financial life. Corning was building a canal at the outlet of Lake Superior, only to come upon an underwater rock ledge which his sandbar dredges could not dent. Harvey had invented a machine for blasting the ledge, and the canal was completed.

Now Corning, former State Senator, former Congressman, member of the peace conference of 1861, former President of the New York Central, Vice Chancellor of the University of New York, went into the Assembly to argue for the grim trestle, the few ugly cars which Charles Harvey loved as some men love fairer creatures.

Corning, seventy-eight years old, eloquent, respected as few men are respected, moved the Assembly to defeat Tweed for the first and only time that session.

"Motion not carried," sang out the speaker.

Harvey could have wept for joy. Mr. Corning's debt had been paid in full. The Ninth Avenue El would stand.

Harvey dropped out of sight after that, as Willson had before him. But his El prospered. A dinner at Delmonico's Restaurant on December 27, 1877, celebrated its success. Cyrus Field, Simeon E. Church and other industrial barons were running things now.

"The El sold out to the sheriff in 1870," announced Field boldly, "but it seems to be doing all right now."

A few minutes later Church stood up and said: "Thank heaven the problem of rapid transit is solved. There will be seats enough for everybody now. Henceforth we shall glide through the air like birds and 'hanging by the strap' [in streetcars and stages] will pass into history."

Harvey made one last appearance before the New York State Legislature. Just before his death in 1913, a very old man, he tottered up to the rostrum to explain his new invention, the dual system, a plan for improved, noiseless Els. Few of the delegates had ever heard of Charles Harvey, or knew his contribution. He was stooped, white-haired and his voice cracked, and doubtless some bored delegate turned to a colleague and said: "Who's the old geezer?"

By then subways were the thing. The father of the elevated railways of the world spoke, but no one listened.

6. Mr. Beach's Marvelous Pneumatic Subway

SUDDENLY, one fine morning, New York woke up and found that it had a subway.

It was all a little crazy, brilliant and unbelievable.

The date was February 19, 1870. New Yorkers read about it in their morning papers.

"Fashionable Reception Held in the Bowels of the Earth!" headlined the incredulous *Herald*.

"The waiting room is a large and elegantly furnished apartment, cheerful and attractive throughout," cooed the *Sun*.

Crowed the *Scientific American*: "This means the end of street dust of which uptown residents get not only their fill, but more than their fill, so that it runs over and collects on their hair, their beards, their eyebrows and floats in their dress like the vapor on a frosty morning. Such discomforts will never be found in the tunnel!"

The subway's waiting room alone astonished the press. Its frescoed walls, elegant paintings, grand piano, bubbling fountain, and goldfish tank—all were ecstatically described. Then there was the single little car, called "spacious" (it sat twenty-two) and "richly upholstered."

But most of all the press was overwhelmed by the great blowing machine which propelled the car, which sent it "skimming along the track like a sail before the wind," and which would, once the car had reached the end of the track, calmly suck it back again!

For this was the Beach Pneumatic Subway. Its only power was air.

What the journalists saw that day, and what 400,000 gawking tourists were to see during the next year, was a cylindrical tube nine feet in diameter, fitting almost as snugly around the single car as a gun barrel around a bullet. A track was laid along the bottom of the tube for 312 feet under the center of Broadway. When the giant fan, called the Roots Patent Force Blast Blower, was turned on, it wafted the car down the track at speeds up to ten miles an hour. At the end of the track the car tripped a wire. This reversed the fan which now "inhaled" the car at the same speed.

The press was excited, so was the public. Not only was the new subway both marvelous and revolutionary, not only did it promise a quick and wondrously unexpected end to the dreadful conditions of street travel—but it caught a shocked city entirely by surprise.

For the Beach Pneumatic Subway was a secret until the moment of its unveiling. No one even suspected it was there. During fifty-eight successive nights it had been burrowed furtively through the earth twenty-one feet under Broadway. While the city slept, men stole out of the growing tunnel to dump bags of dirt into wagons whose wheels had been muffled for silence. Other wagons arrived bringing tools, rails, bricks for the tunnel walls, parts for the car and for the mighty wind machine. Night after night gangs of men slipped in and out of the tunnel like thieves. The street surface was undisturbed. All day, traffic of the busiest thoroughfare of the New World thundered over Mr. Beach's tunnel. At night the clip-clop of an occasional hansom cab was plainly audible to the workers beneath.

Now, Beach himself led groups of dignitaries on inspection tours of the tunnel. He was a small frail man with straw-colored hair, clean-shaven, with deep-set eyes, a long thin nose and a long upper lip. Forty-four years old, he was well known as an inventor, patent lawyer and publisher.

"We propose to run the line to Central Park, about five miles in all," he would say. "When completed we should be able to carry twenty thousand passengers a day at speeds up to a mile a minute."

A mile a minute? His listeners gasped. In 1870 nothing went that fast.

When they discovered the existence of the subway, city politicians were enraged. Beach had received permission to construct a small tube only, to see if a pneumatic dispatch service might prove practical. By building a subway instead he had willfully defied them. There was talk of destroying the tunnel, of throwing Beach into jail.

Beach, knowing the power and determination of his opposition—Boss Tweed and the Tammany Ring, was nervous, but steadfast.

"New York needs a subway," he insisted. "I will go before the Legislature at Albany."

No one had ever stood up to Tweed in this way before and, furious, he swore to stop Beach no matter what it cost him. The quarrel was more than personal. All streetcar companies paid tribute to Tweed. The new subway threatened that monopoly.

The Beach Transit Bill came to a vote in January, 1871, backed by overwhelming popular support.

Tweed was ready with a rapid transit bill of his own. It was called the Viaduct Plan Bill.

Beach's subway called for the expenditure of just over $5,-000,000, all raised privately.

Tweed's Viaduct Plan was to cost $80,000,000, five of it to be posted at once by the state to be used in any way the directors of the campany saw fit. (At this time New York City was still paying for its County Courthouse. Begun by Tweed in 1868 on a budget of $250,000, it was still unfinished in 1871 and had already cost over $8,000,000, including $641,000 for carpets, $1,937,545 for plastering and $2,960,187 for furniture.)

All work on the Beach subway would be conducted underground, without disturbing the street.

Tweed's Viaduct Plan would climb the length of the island on great stone arches forty feet high. Everything underneath would be condemned and razed.

"Spaghetti"—wires, cables, pipes—must be rearranged after a construction job.

Now in January, 1871, the New York State Senate passed the Beach Transit Bill by a vote of 22 to 5. The bill's margin in the Assembly was even wider, 102 to 11.

But the Legislature, known throughout the state as Tweed's "Black Horse Cavalry," also approved the Viaduct Plan.

The bills arrived simultaneously on the desk of Governor John T. Hoffman.

All of New York waited impatiently. Would the marvelous invention of Mr. Beach be officially sanctioned? Would he be permitted to build the subway which New York needed, and now wanted so desperately?

Or would Boss Tweed go on looting the city (his new instrument this Viaduct Plan), while hour by hour, day by day, traffic in the streets grew thicker and thicker, snarled and tangled beyond all reason, even pedestrians having to push and shove to get through?

In a few hours the anxious city would know.

According to all the signs by which men make such judgments, Alfred Eli Beach was a genius.

He was a man of vision, originality, quick perception and fantastic energy. Among his dozens of inventions were the cable railway, the pneumatic tube and the hydraulic tunneling bore by which his own tunnel was burrowed under Broadway, as well as later tunnels under London's Thames River, Glasgow's Clyde and New York's Hudson.

He seems never to have known a childhood, in the ordinary sense. Before he was twenty-one he had invented the world's first practical typewriter. Made of wood, it was as unattractive as a bushel basket, and about the same size, but it worked, winning the gold medal at the Crystal Palace Exposition in 1853. Young as he was, Beach knew full well what he had done.

"Someday," he predicted, "boys will be taught to write their names only. All the rest will be played on this literary piano."

He was a compassionate man, deeply moved by suffering. To him, a man locked up in darkness by blindness seemed to suffer most of all. So Beach worked almost ten years trying to adapt his typewriter to imprint a raised type which the blind

could read with their fingers. At last he had it, male and female
dies arranged to strike simultaneously on opposite sides of the
paper, thus embossing a character.

Like many men of his type, he was patient with problems
but bored by success. Once an invention was finished, he had
no time for it, and would go on to something else. He earned
a little money from some of his inventions, but nothing at all
from most of them. Remington and others made fortunes in
his wake. Beach himself would have remained poor if invention had been his only source of income.

But for most of his life he managed three careers simultaneously, publisher, inventor and patent lawyer. He was only
nineteen when he took over a run-down and financially shaky
journal called the *Scientific American*. In a few years he had
built it into the most successful, powerful and influential
weekly of its type. It was to become a beacon of light in an
age which otherwise might not have been ready for the astound-
ing scientific advances it was to know.

At twenty-two, Beach became publisher, with his brother,
of the New York *Sun*, his father's paper, first and most lucrative of the city's penny dailies. By the time he was twenty-six
the *Sun* had ceased to stimulate him, so he stepped out, leaving control to his brother. In all he founded a score or more
publications, some of them still on America's newsstands today.

He was indefatigable. Between 1850 and 1860 he endured
the bumpy day-and-a-half ride to Washington every two weeks,
taking the ferry across the Hudson and boarding the train on
the Jersey side. On behalf of struggling inventors he argued
thousands of patent cases, winning virtually all of them.

Inventors, good or bad, loved him. He was always courteous,
always patient, always had time to listen, even to the most
hare-brained scheme, and afterwards to offer advice and occasional financial aid.

He gave encouragement and a friendly ear to Elias Howe,
Samuel F. B. Morse, R. J. Gatling (inventor of the machine
gun) and to Captain John Ericson who was soon to launch
the *Monitor*.

Tom Edison was a frequent visitor, and it was to Alfred
Beach's desk that he first brought his new phonograph.

"What is it?" asked Beach.

"It's my talking box," said Edison.

For a moment, while Edison grinned at him with pride, Beach gazed at the handle which jutted from the box.

"Well," said Beach, "cranks are made for cranking," and he began to turn the handle.

"Good morning, sir," said the machine. "How are you? How do you like the talking box?"

When not at his desk, Beach would be in his workshop. He had no time for vacations, and never took one. His life was regulated to its smallest detail. He knew a week in advance what clothes he would wear, what food he would eat, what moment he would arrive at the office. That way there would always be time for everything, he would never be rushed, never thrown off stride. He allowed time for inventors who imposed upon him, for evenings with his family (he had no taste for society) and for exercise, which he believed related directly to good health. He was never sick.

He read widely and thoroughly and could speak with imagination and originality on many subjects. His quick, incisive mind was never satisfied with the superficial. The salient points he grasped at once. From there he probed deeper, ever deeper. He had no interest in gossip or polite conversation, only in ideas.

He got by on a few hours' sleep a night. He was a kind man, a gentle man, but a restless one. He was always working on half a dozen things at once. Music was his only relaxation. He loved opera particularly, and attended it often.

It was in 1849, when Alfred Beach was only twenty-three years old, that he first conceived the idea of a subway. Beach's office overlooked City Hall, one of the busiest sections of the city. Day after day the noise of frightened horses and cracking whips floated up to him. So did the voices of the drivers cursing pedestrians, cursing each other. There was the occasional crack of clubs against skulls as police used primitive methods for untangling jams.

Beach himself lived far uptown at 9 West Twentieth Street. It took him almost an hour to get home each night.

There were only two possibilities for relieving street congestion, an elevated road or a subway. Though he was later to build an experimental El, Beach was disinclined to favor them, reasoning that they would be noisy, unsightly and, most of all, dangerous.

For the most dependable motive power in 1849 was a team of strong horses. But horses were skittish creatures which shied and bolted at the least fright. On a trestle ten or more feet above the street there would be no controlling them at all. Dozens of unlucky passengers would plunge to their deaths each year.

But a subway—the idea sent a thrill through him. He could not get enough of imagining such a grandiose scheme.

"The plan is to tunnel Broadway its entire length," he wrote in the *Scientific American,* in what was possibly the world's first public projection of the subway concept, "with openings at every corner. There would be two tracks, with a footpath running between them, the whole to be brilliantly lighted with gas. The cars, to be drawn by horses, would stop ten seconds at every corner."

A decade and a half passed, during which Beach pushed the subway idea as best he could in *Scientific American* and New York *Sun* editorials.

Then in 1866 he began his experiments with pneumatic power. An even grander subway plan began to take shape in his mind.

Today, as attempts are being made to reach the moon, Beach's faith in pneumatic power seems incredibly naïve. But in 1866, pneumatic power promised the only hope for a subway—and New York, it seemed to Beach, had to have a subway. The electric and gasoline engines having not yet been invented, Beach's only alternative was to bury a great steam locomotive and have it pull the subway cars.

Impossible, thought Beach. People would never ride in a tunnel with those soot-belching monsters. White shirts would be turned black by the smoke. Cinders would fly in the windows and set fire to ladies' garments. Besides, too many boilers burst far too frequently. An explosion would mean a cave-in. Those who weren't scalded to death by escaping steam would be buried alive. One such disaster would mean the end of the subway for all time.

It *had* to be pneumatic power. Beach knew of course that the wind machines of his day were inadequate. But he was a dreamer and he imagined more compact, more powerful fans, then turbines as mighty as jet engines. One day, he thought, subways would whoosh under the streets at speeds considered fantastic!

When the American Institute Fair was held in the Fourteenth Street Armory in 1867, Beach installed a plywood tube six feet in diameter which ran the length of the armory, and into it inserted a small car with seats for ten passengers. A Helix fan, ten feet in diameter, funneled a blast of air into the tube, blowing the car with great élan from Fourteenth to Fifteenth streets, then drawing it back again. Hundreds of passengers rode in this car during succeeding weeks, and the exhibit often won spontaneous applause.

Beach now knew that it was possible to propel a train through a pneumatic tube.

He went to work to devise a machine for boring a tunnel without disturbing the surface of the street.

His hydraulic tunneling shield, when completed, somewhat resembled a barrel with both ends punched out. The front end was sharp for cutting through earth, and the back end was extremely thin so that the newly dug tunnel could be bricked up from *inside* the shield, the workers being protected at all times. Pistons would then press against the completed brick to drive the cutting edge forward another sixteen to eighteen inches into the earth. That much dirt would be gouged out by diggers and removed. The pistons worked individually; by exerting pressure on one side or the other, the tunnel could be made to turn in the earth, or to climb or descend, according to the will of the engineer.

Beach now determined to seek a charter from the Legislature, if not actually to build a subway, then to build something enough like one so that a subway tunnel might be bored secretly.

He had conducted a number of experiments on pneumatic mail tubes. One of his schemes was to have mail, deposited in a hollow lamppost, flutter down into a small tunnel, where a blast of air would blow it along until it dropped down a chute into a distributing station.

At the distributing station the letters would be sorted and placed in cylinders to be whisked through underground pneumatic tubes to their destinations, thus providing unprecedented speed in mail service.

In line with this plan, Beach dispatched some agents to map the streets, and sent others armed with the crude instruments of the day to sound Manhattan along certain key thoroughfares. What lay below the pavement? Beach said he was interested in Broadway particularly, to a depth of twenty feet.

"Twenty feet?" asked one technician, surprised. "Why so deep?"

"Just an idea," replied Beach, as if preoccupied.

In 1868, Beach's petition for a postal dispatch charter went before the Legislature, crossing the desk of Boss Tweed, who ignored it. It looked innocent enough, reasoned Tweed. Tweed had no quarrel with the U. S. Mail, nor did he have any plans to swindle it.

The charter was granted by the Legislature.

Beach was a shrewd observer of the political climate. He had watched the downfall of several men who had opposed Tammany, and now he decided against seeking a franchise for a subway. He believed he had sanction enough to build one anyway—particularly if no one knew he was doing it.

"I won't pay political blackmail," he told his brother. "I say, let's build the subway furtively."

His associates were nervous. Who knew what reprisals Tammany might choose to make, when the tunnel became known. The risk was too great.

But Beach rode over objections. Let the subway be built well enough and no one could stop it, not Tweed himself!

The soundings had indicated a strata of sand under Murray Street at Broadway, offering no obstacles to the tunneling shield. It was decided to begin work there. Accordingly, the basement of Devlin's Clothing Store was rented, and, one night in 1868, the first load of dirt was dragged across the cellar and dumped in the far corner.

Foreman of the gang was Beach's son, Fred, then twenty-one years old. Night after night the digging proceeded smoothly. Then, as the tunnel lengthened, some of the men became frightened by the eerie depths and did not return to work. The air was close in the tunnel, the lantern light cast flickering shadows on the wall, and the horses clip-clopping overhead made a weirdly hollow sound. If a man was not careful, all testified, he could easily be spooked down there.

One night the tunneling bore rang against stone.

None had been expected. Bit by bit in the lantern light picks chipped away at the earth until an entire wall was exposed. It filled the whole face of the shield!

"It looks like the foundation of an old fort," said an awed voice.

"What do we do now?" asked another.

Young Beach swallowed hard. "Better get Pop down here right away," he said.

A cab was sent galloping through the night to rout Alfred Beach from his bed. Half-dressed, worried, Beach rushed from his house just as dawn was beginning to lighten the streets and buildings of Manhattan.

When he arrived in the tunnel, lanterns were held close while Beach examined the wall.

"If we remove that," stated someone decisively, "the street will collapse."

All awaited Beach's decision. Inside the shield the men would be safe, whatever happened. But suppose the street did collapse? Beach imagined hordes of citizens peering down at the suddenly exposed diggers. I'd be like a man found naked in public, he thought. I'd be ruined.

A while longer he gazed at the wall by the flickering light. Then he made his decision.

"Remove it, stone by stone."

The tunnel bored on. It was a number of days before Beach could watch calmly while traffic thundered over the undermined spot. He feared to see a sudden sagging in the street, and a loaded omnibus or streetcar go pitching into the hole.

But the tunnel held.

Work went on under Broadway.

Although the digging was finished in fifty-eight nights, the better part of two years and $350,000 of Beach's own money were used to make ready the showpiece which Beach at last exhibited to the public in February, 1870.

That the subway must be lavish, even beautiful (if tunnels can be beautiful) Beach had long since decided. People would be reluctant to accept something new, even something they knew they needed desperately. Popular support, and he needed overwhelming popular support to overcome Tammany Hall, could be won only by a subway which was both practical and elegant, one which would please the gourmets and the merely hungry alike. Unlike most men of his type, Beach knew that genius without salesmanship was not enough. Steak alone was simply—steak. The sauce was the thing.

And so, over the objections of his partners, he had the waiting room extended to 120 feet—almost half as long as the tunnel itself—and installed the grand piano, the paintings, the fountain and the goldfish tank. To counter the dismay of visitors entering the "bowels of the earth" for the first time, Beach decreed the zircon lamps. All must be as bright, as gay, as jaunty even, as possible.

White with rage, official New York looked on as the subway opened. Alfred Eli Beach, small, frail and nervous, but absolutely dedicated to a subway for New York, girded himself for the battle of his life.

In 1870, William Marcy Tweed, State Senator, Grand Sachem of Tammany Hall, strode aggressively across the summit of the greatest concentration of civic power in New York's history. Diamonds flashed on his fingers and on the head of his tiepin, and his eyes glittered coldly.

Only nineteen years before he had come before the city courts a bankrupt, but now his wealth was incalculable.

He was loud, bold and rich. He owned lavish city and country residences, a stable of race horses and acre upon acre of property. With a crony, James H. Ingersol, he controlled a furniture company which provided $50 sofas or desks for the city—at $5,000 apiece. His New York Printing Company printed the city's forms, and those of every insurance company too. It had absorbed three other companies larger than itself, and four smaller because it had succeeded in cornering the market—the insurance companies were afraid not to do business with Tweed.

Tweed's Manufacturing Stationers' Company furnished supplies for the city's schools. In April of 1870 it had delivered fourteen reams of paper, twenty-four pen holders, four ink bottles, twelve sponges to be used for blotting ink, three dozen boxes of rubber bands and six rulers—and then had sent a bill for $10,000 which Schools Commissioner William Marcy Tweed had promptly paid.

Other outrageous bills were submitted by Tweed's street cleaning companies which never cleaned any streets at all, which did not, in fact, even own a broom. These, too, were promptly paid, because New York's Deputy Street Commissioner (William Marcy Tweed) never thought to question them.

Tweed was no one-man gang. The Tammany Ring was well organized and it is estimated that it stole between forty-five and two hundred million dollars from the city between 1869 and 1871 alone.

All this was possible because Tweed controlled the Democratic political machines of both the city and the state. Born in New York on April 3, 1823, he had begun his career as the roughest brawler on the roughest fire company in the city. With these sterling qualifications he was judged worthy to run for Alderman in 1852 and, in a one-party city, he won. Two years later he was even sent to Washington as a Congressman.

Tweed's real power began with his election to the city's Board of Supervisors in 1857, during the reign of the notoriously corrupt Mayor, Fernando Wood. Wood was so corrupt he was actually tottering, and, with one good shove from Tweed, he fell. All of New York cheered the downfall of Wood, and the rise of Honest Bill Tweed.

Encouraged by the success of his honesty, Tweed grabbed control of the Board of Supervisors and began making "astute" political appointments. Soon Tweed men were everywhere, and the city began to be systematically sacked.

Before long the Ring was so rich that there was literally

nothing it could not buy. It bought co-operation from legitimate businesses, it even bought success at the polls. The fix was in and no election was safe. The Ring bribed those men who counted votes, it bribed those assigned to guard the ballot boxes. It bought gangs of bewildered immigrants who were rounded up, sworn in as citizens and herded to the polls. It bought the State Assembly in 1866, it bought the Mayor of the city, a wisecracking playboy named A. Oakey Hall, and, in 1868, it forced the election of the Governor, John T. Hoffman.

"Stick with me," Tweed told Hoffman, "and you'll be the Democratic nominee for President in 1872."

And now in March, 1871, there was no dramatic showdown between Boss Tweed and Alfred Eli Beach. Tweed's Viaduct Plan and the Beach Transit Bill, both approved by the Legislature, arrived on Hoffman's desk. Hoffman, having received his instructions from Tweed, merely signed the one and vetoed the other.

And that was that.

The newspapers were enraged. The two bills had reached Hoffman not twenty-four hours before, it was charged. He could not even have had time to read them!

The veto, cried a *Tribune* editorial, "was long since prepared. Of course it was to be expected that, as long as Tammany had no hand in the scheme and saw no chance of converting it into a swindle, its influence would be used against it; but for the sake of decency, the tracks might have been covered up."

Beach himself breathed a long sigh of regret. His associates were bitterly disappointed.

"It's all right," he told them soothingly. "It's all right. We might have expected that. The veto means we must wait another year, nothing more. By next year we will have support so strong that our bill will pass even over the Governor's veto!"

And so for a year, with young Fred Beach as conductor and brakeman, the little car was blown back and forth every day under Broadway. There were two types of passengers, the thrill seekers who hurried down the steps to Devlin's basement, and the merely curious who entered the waiting room more cautiously. Both types arrived in great numbers, and often police lines were necessary to hold back the mobs. Devlin sold a lot of clothes during the long waits. The lines moved slowly. After each ride, passengers were permitted to leave the car and stroll along the narrow tunnel. This was considered highly exciting. More than one sweet young thing proved her daring to her beau by joining him on the floor of the tunnel.

For a year the car traveled, its progress obvious to all who passed near the ventilator grating at the corner of Murray Street. A fountain stood close to the grating, its bubbling water blown into spray two stories high every time the giant fan underground went into reverse. The fan's intake was just as powerful—letters, parcels, handkerchiefs were yanked from people's hands, hats were pulled from their heads, and all the refuse of the neighborhood was sucked against the grate. A moment later all would be blown sky-high again as the little car below made its return journey. It was a corner people learned to stay clear of.

During that year Beach made every effort to keep his subway in the news, and he sought to coax dignitaries to ride in it so that reports would find their way into the newspapers. But he had little luck. With Tweed against him, no city or state official would come near the place. He had to settle for Secretary of the Navy Robeson, who praised the subway in a pathetic little story which all the papers carried in mid-1872.

The subway had made money. At a quarter a head it had earned more than $100,000, which Beach, with a great show of confidence, promptly handed over to charity. This was a magnificent gesture, but a hollow one, for Beach's courage was wearing thin. At the beginning of the new year he waited, his heart thumping irregularly, as the Beach Transit Bill came to a vote a second time.

It passed. Beach had spent a fortune keeping lobbyists at Albany all the preceding year, and he had expected it would.

Hoffman vetoed it again and it was returned to the Legislature, where it failed by one vote to attain the two-thirds majority needed to pass over the Governor's veto.

That night Beach wept his defeat. But in the morning he was himself again.

"We'll try once more," he told his associates. "Perhaps there will be a new governor next year."

Beach closed the subway; as crowds fell off it began to cost too much to run it. But he kept his lobbyists in Albany.

There were encouraging signs as 1872 drew to a close. A bookkeeper had placed evidence of Tweed's swindles in the hands of the New York *Times*, which had proceeded to print the disclosures day after day. Tweed had been indicted for fraud. It now appeared that his political power would be ended.

On election day, 1872, the people of New York State, filled with righteous indignation, threw out John T. Hoffman.

The long fight had worn Beach down. Where he had been stanch he now was timid. Some people had criticized his bill on the grounds that pneumatic power would never prove satisfactory; others had insisted that the tunneling shield would never work except in sandy areas. Beach had the charter rewritten, making provisions for steam locomotives, if they should prove more practical, and for the cut-and-fill method of entrenching a subway, if his shield should fail.

There was nothing he could do about the chief objection to his subway, the fear that Trinity Church (then the tallest structure in the city) and other "mighty spires," would topple if Broadway was tunneled. This was something which John Jacob Astor and other wealthy landlords had been shouting at the top of their lungs for two years now. Trinity Church's spire was 280 feet tall.

And so in 1873 the Beach Transit Bill came before the Legislature of the Sovereign State of New York for the third and last time. It was passed by acclamation, there being only three dissents in the Senate, and was sent in to the new Governor, General John A. Dix, who announced himself "pleased and privileged" to sign it.

That night the elation of Beach and his associates was boundless. They had fought a long, tense war, but they appeared to have won.

"We've done it," Beach cried over and over again. "We've done it."

But his joy was short lived. Beach himself was emotionally

exhausted. Astor and the others were against him; and they were much more vocal than he. Worse, his own fortune now was gone, spent on lobbyists, publicity and the construction of the experimental tunnel itself.

Prices had risen. He was forced to raise not five, but ten million dollars before work could be started. He began to make the rounds of wealthy businessmen, former friends. But he was no longer one of them. He had become, it seemed to them, just another penniless inventor begging funds, pushing some wild scheme nobody cared about. People would never ride in the ground anyway.

And then the economy, none too steady since the great depression of 1869, began to flounder. The stock market crashed again, and there was suddenly no money to be had at all.

One day Alfred Eli Beach, tired beyond words, beaten at last, admitted to himself that he had failed. There was no money. There never would be any money.

Late in 1873, with the "greatest reluctance," Governor Dix withdrew the charter.

The Beach Pneumatic Subway would never be built.

For a long while after that Alfred Beach was a crushed, heartbroken man. His depression seemed bottomless. When he came out of it finally he was a different person. His friends remarked that his conversations were less stimulating, his observations less acute, and rarely witty. He seemed kinder, gentler than ever before, particularly to those earnest young men who arrived at his desk bearing their latest contraptions.

The vigor was gone. He had stopped inventing.

His new interest was publishing. He started one new journal after the other, most of them curious inbreedings of the *Scientific American* itself: *The Science Record, The Scientific American Supplement* (which printed the complete texts of the weightiest scientific papers of the day), and *La America Cientifica*, which was published in Spanish and distributed throughout Central and South America. Beach had taught himself Spanish. He loved the language and he was proud and delighted on the day *La America Cientifica* finally began to make money.

He was an easy touch for charities during those years, for there was great love in him for humble people, for those who had been destroyed by life. One of his chief projects, once on his financial feet again, was the Beach Institute in Savannah which he endowed, and which furnished a free education for freed slaves. He felt no bitterness toward any man, not even toward the convicted Tweed who reposed in Ludlow Street Jail, and who died there in 1878.

Beach became devoutly religious. Born a Presbyterian, he greatly admired the celebrated Henry Ward Beecher, pastor of the Plymouth Church in Brooklyn. But Brooklyn was hours away from home by hansom cab. Beach could not have attended Sunday services. With Beecher's permission, he had a private telephone wire installed, connecting his home with Beecher's pulpit, so that he could listen to the eloquent preacher every Sunday. He would invite his friends over to join him in worship, he would pass hymn books around, and all would join in the singing.

Gradually the pneumatic subway was forgotten, and with it Alfred Beach himself. When he died of pneumonia on New Year's Day, 1896, at the age of sixty-nine, he had faded totally from the public view. His obituary in the New York *Times* ran only a few inches and attracted hardly any notice.

There is a small postscript to the story. In February, 1912, workers cutting the new BMT subway broke suddenly, unexpectedly into Beach's tunnel. All was as it had been forty years before, when Beach had ordered it sealed up. Some of the wooden fixtures had rotted, but the air was dry and warm and the tunnel was in good condition. Alongside the once-elegant station the little car stood on its rails, as if waiting patiently for its next load of passengers. The tunneling bore still plugged one end of the tunnel, waiting to be driven forward—toward the end of the island.

Today Beach's tube is part of the BMT's City Hall Station, and there is a small plaque on one wall which acknowledges Beach as the father of New York's 726 thundering miles of subway. He was one of the giants of America's mechanical age, but this is the only public recognition he ever got.

7. Deathblow to Subways

THERE WERE TWO other subway plans proposed during the seventies, both somewhat wild. One was called the Arcade Railway, and sought to excavate Broadway from one side of the street to the other to a depth of twenty feet. Two tracks, with sidewalks on both sides, were then to be put down, and the whole thing was to be roofed over in glass. Normal street traffic would continue overhead, the sun filtering down upon the "arcade" through the legs of horses and people, and past the rather substantial bulk of vehicular New York. Sub-basements fronting on to the Arcade would now become chic shops, transforming dingy storage space into valuable property. This plan was not received with much enthusiasm anywhere.

The other belonged to the Metropolitan Transit Company and was introduced by a reasonably competent ex-state engineer named James B. Swain in 1872. Swain envisioned a triple railroad, one line running on top of the other. There would be a subway for freight cars, a "depressed" road for passenger cars, and an El to catch the overflow. The El would hang suspended from its trestle and would be dragged along by horses.

Swain wanted to cut through blocks (as had Tweed's defunct Viaduct Plan), not up a north-south avenue, and said that west of Sixth Avenue up to 179th Street would be best. It seems incredible that a man as intelligent as Swain could believe with apparent sincerity in an undertaking as expensive as this one would have been, or that the Legislature would give it the green light, which it did. But a capital stock of $5,000,-

ooo was all that was authorized, which never would have been enough. Swain, however, failed to raise even that much, though he worked at it for several years.

And so New York, denied a subway, turned instead to another El. This one was called the Gilbert Patent Railway, in honor of its founder, Rufus Henry Gilbert, and was built along Sixth Avenue as far north as Central Park between March, 1876, and June, 1878.

Gilbert, a strange, intense man, was a doctor. One of the renowned surgeons of his time, he became a railroad man for strictly humanitarian reasons.

He was born January 26, 1832, in Guilford, New York, and became successively a druggist's apprentice, a machinist (for six years), a scholar (classical literature and mathematics), and finally a medical student so skillful that he attracted the notice of Dr. Willard Parker, Dean of New York's College of Physicians and Surgeons.

Railroads, and Els in particular, were something Gilbert more or less stumbled upon. Leaving medical school without a degree, he began to practice surgery in Corning, New York, where he cured so many apparently hopeless patients that he soon was working seventy to eighty hours a week. Under such harsh strain his health broke, and he was advised to go to Europe to recuperate.

There he studied hospital management, first in London, then in Paris, remarking that the vast majority of patients in both places were products of slum areas. When he began to investigate, he could conclude only that disease was bred by the fetid air and lack of sunlight of the slums. Fired by compassion, he reasoned that the poor of the world could be saved by the hundreds of thousands if only some fast, convenient method of transport could be found to take them out of the tenements into the clean, refreshing beauty of the country.

The most miserable of them would then be able to commute to the city to work. A good railroad could save millions of lives, more than could a dozen new drugs.

Excited by his new rapid transit idea, Dr. Gilbert returned to New York determined to work out the methods and gadgets needed to mount a railroad above the streets, a fast, cheap railroad which would carry the poor forever away from the death by plague which awaited them in the city.

But the Civil War broke out. Surgeons were needed and Dr. Gilbert reluctantly decided that rapid transit would have to wait. Joining the Union's Duryée's Zouaves, he started as medical inspector at Fortress Monroe, then was attached to the Fourteenth Army in the field. His skill and his willingness to attend wounded men under fire won him fame and promotion, and at the battle of Big Bethel he performed the first surgical operation ever done under battle conditions. He had risen to lieutenant colonel when the war ended, but again the strain had broken his health.

In 1865 he took a job as assistant superintendent of the Century Railroad of New Jersey, hoping to gain practical experience before advancing his rapid transit ideas. He remodeled the Century road, gained wide notice, then resigned. Henceforth all his time and energy would be devoted to rapid transit.

At this time (1866) no Els had yet been built, (only Charles Harvey was known to be working on one) or subways either. Hundreds of devices had to be conceived and executed by Gilbert before his first stanchion could rise. He early decided to use steam locomotives, not Harvey's cable system, only to have Boss Tweed charge loudly that the locomotives would "scare the horses and drop live coals in the streets." Dr. Gilbert shook his head doggedly and designed a "drip pan" to catch coals and other debris, and a dummy façade which masked the locomotives, muffling the noise and, presumably, causing horses to think the locomotives were not locomotives at all.

One by one, the ex-surgeon's inventions were completed and seven major patents secured, including automatic safety gimmicks and a method for keeping the swaying cars from falling into the street. By June of 1872, after six long years of work, Gilbert was ready to attack the Legislature for a charter.

He was lucky. The Legislature, concerned with the Beach Transit Bill, Harvey's bankrupt Ninth Avenue El, and the imminent conviction of Tweed, gave Gilbert's bill only passing attention and a quick, affirmative vote.

Now, when all Dr. Gilbert had to do was raise money, the crash of 1873 all but wiped him out. The years began to pass; Gilbert was still unable to find backers.

Early in 1876 the previous year's receipts of the now-prosperous Ninth Avenue El were published. Though its two- or three-car trains did not run at all on Sundays, though it took thirty-five minutes to run from the Battery to Thirty-fourth Street, the line had rung up $82,945—a fantastic average of $265 a day.

Profits such as this on a route less densely populated than the one Gilbert proposed, sent swindlers swarming around him in early 1876. One of them, William Foster, Jr., promised the backing of the New York Loan and Improvement Company. Dr. Gilbert, distraught, approaching desperation after four frustrating years, was willing to listen to anyone. He soon agreed to re-form his company, creating directors, taking in Foster, Jr., as partner, and issuing $3,500,000 in stock.

Foster, Jr., now took up thousands of shares to sell, but didn't sell them. Instead he formed a ring, together with J. T. Navarro and the Loan and Improvement Company, which soon acquired entire control of the El, including even the stock which Dr. Gilbert had counted as his own. Dr. Gilbert, occupied with the hundreds of technical problems of actual construction, filled with joy to see his El mounting block by block up Manhattan, never suspected what was happening.

On June 5, 1878, the Sixth Avenue El, completed to Central Park, was opened to the public. Horses shied and whinnied with fright as the first train made its thundering journey overhead, its smokestack belching smoke, sparks and ashes, its engine leaking water and oil upon the street. The elegant new cars were light green, their upholstery dark brown. Brakemen on each car received signals from the driver and from each other by hand. A conductor took up tickets costing ten cents (five cents for workers during rush hours) which had been threaded with silk as protection against counterfeiting.

Almost the next day Dr. Gilbert found himself voted out of the directorate of his company, and shortly after that he was simply voted out altogether. William Foster, Jr., and J. T. Navarro had taken it all. They in turn were soon forced out by Jay Gould, Russell Sage, Cyrus Field and others, who took over in 1881. Sage, one of the richest men of his time, had a pass printed so he could ride free on the El. It was said that he would dart in the door each morning, having been driven to the nearest station from his uptown mansion, would grab the nearest seat, and would never give it up, not even to aged, obviously infirm ladies. Although this practice would raise no eyebrows today, it did then.

For seven years Dr. Gilbert struggled against opposition, exhausting all that was left of his money in lawsuit after lawsuit, in a pathetic attempt to regain his railroad. It was no good. He died in 1885 at the age of fifty-three, of a broken heart, his friends said. He left a wife, two children and the Sixth Avenue El. Had he lived he would only have been disillusioned. Although the poor, for whom he had had such hopes, used his El for years, it was only for proceeding from the slums to work and then back to the slums. They rarely used it to get away into the country. The slum dwellers of the world have never had much use for the country.

In fact, Dr. Gilbert's El and others made new slums where none had been before, made dingy, sunless streets of what had been broad avenues. A subway would have spared the city that at least. Sixth Avenue later became notorious for sin. Under the shadow of the El, saloons, dance halls and brothels sprang up, places like the French Madame's, the Cremone and the Haymarket. Thugs and prostitutes stalked the street and a man found that neither his morals nor his pocketbook were safe there. Finally the Reverend T. DeWitt Talmadge, a Brooklyn preacher, spoke out against Sixth Avenue's "gaslit carnival of vice." He called it "Satan's Circus." The name stuck until a better one replaced it. Police Inspector Williams, a cop with his hand out, was transferred there from a quiet district. The payoff to dishonest cops along Sixth Avenue was enough to make a man heady.

"I've been living on rump steak," cracked Williams. "Now I'm eating tenderloin."

After that, Sixth Avenue was known as the Tenderloin.

For years men were stationed in the streets under the Els to warn horsemen of the approach of trains. Riding the Els was considered highly dangerous. Two brothers, international bankers, never rode the same train. Thus, if one were killed in a wreck, the other could carry on the business. Once the brothers looked up suddenly to find themselves sitting opposite each other. They panicked. One ran to the first car, the other to the last.

Men known for bravery were frightened by their first ride on an El. Eugene Schuyler, just back from dangerous explorations in Turkistan, was made ill when his Ninth Avenue train, at thirty miles an hour, moved out onto the towering curved trestle at the northern boundary of Central Park. Whimpering, he begged to be returned to the city some other way.

Crude cartoons were produced by the witty and the morbid, and they appeared everywhere in the early eighties.

"While waiting for trains," one was captioned, "passengers can amuse themselves by reading the signs in the waiting room." The drawing showed the signs: Insure your life before going on board—$3000 in event of death; A competent surgeon always on board; Bandages may be procured from Conductor; Convenient hospitals established along line.

Other cartoons of the day showed clothes, drying on the housetops, getting the benefit of "smoke and cinders"; pedestrians below having the engineer "dump the firebox" on them; and passengers being "treated to a bath" when the train kept right on going at the Battery and shot off into the river.

Nonetheless, the subways which might have been were forgotten, for the Els were overwhelmingly popular. Within a year five hundred homes had been built north of Fiftieth Street. There were soon so many riders that the rule whereby you paid only if you found a seat, had to be suspended—"temporarily." Soon there were Els along Second and Third avenues too, and all New York was singing a new hit song by A. H. Rosewig. It was called "The Rapid Transit Gallop."

The last of Dr. Gilbert's El was torn down at 10:52 AM on April 7, 1939. While subways rumbled underground, Mayor Fiorello H. La Guardia mounted a ladder carrying a welding torch and burned out the last ceremonial rivet of the last standing section of the line.

A few months later La Guardia performed the same rite at Ninth and Second avenues too, but now he was balanced precariously on the ladder and somebody called, "The ladder's too straight, sir."

"That's all right," joked La Guardia, "this is a straight administration."

The crowd laughed, then applauded, as the fat little man clambered down.

Soon scrap steel was all that was left of the Sixth Avenue El, and that was sold at public auction on the steps of City Hall on a rainy morning in December. The buyer was George Weissbaum, who presented business cards from San Francisco, Seattle and Denver, but who proved to be known in none of those places. The El of the humanitarian doctor later was dropped on American troops in the Pacific, by guns and planes of imperial Japan.

Mayor La Guardia, an aide, and Comptroller Joseph McGoldrick came out onto the steps in the rain to meet the successful bidder. A crowd of about a dozen, standing under umbrellas, had stopped to watch, and the aide sang out: "Three cheers for the best Mayor and best Comptroller we've ever had!"

No one was thinking about the Sixth Avenue El, or cared what became of it. It had been a mistake anyway. It should have been a subway.

A soggy cheer went up.

8. Birth Pangs of the IRT

FINALLY NEW YORK DID get a subway. The first section of it was built between March 24, 1900, and Oct. 27, 1904, by August Belmont, financier, and John B. McDonald, contractor, at a cost of $35,000,000. The actual construction was an engineering marvel of the most thrilling sort which, however, cost many men their lives. Others escaped unhurt from experiences which can only be called bizarre.

There was nothing subtle about the subway when it did come. Gangs of men, truckloads of dynamite, giant derricks and digging machines simply came in and tore the streets out by the roots. Traffic stopped, business stopped, it was as if the life blood of the city had stopped. In some places overpasses made rickety bridges across the gaping wound in the hide of the island. In other places there were no overpasses—and no movement either. One of the areas most severely affected was Forty-second Street, which was laid open from Seventh Avenue to Lexington. Merchants wailed from dawn till dark, for few customers were willing to clamber over pipes, cables, ditches and other obstructions to reach their doors. Some merchants tried giant sales to stimulate business, some went on as before to a greatly reduced clientele, some simply threw up their hands and closed altogether.

For two years workers gouged a great open trench almost the length of Manhattan. Then the decked method of construction came in. Now, once the initial incision had been made, a deck of planks and timbers would be thrown over it, the trolley tracks laid down as before, and life could proceed more or less normally aboveground. Under it, men burrowed ever deeper and wider, shoring up the deck with additional supports whenever necessary.

The new method made work on the subway darker, slower and more hazardous. Suppose gas escaped from a main or sewer pipe and, in the confined space below, a pick rang against stone, and a spark flickered in the gloom—boom! Workers were so afraid of explosions that mains and sewers had to be diverted to run outside, usually on a wooden trestle above the street, or lying against the curb covered with boards.

Just after noon on January 27, 1902, there was an explosion, but not from gas. In a storage shed over the cut at Forty-first Street and Park Avenue, a twenty-eight-year-old powderman named Moses Epps sat warming his hands over a lighted candle—a few feet away from 548 pounds of dynamite. Testimony later disclosed that Epps stepped outside for a few minutes. When he re-entered he found that the candle had tumbled to the floor and ignited the paper which had wrapped his lunch. The floor itself was now blazing merrily, Epps ran for a bucket of water, sloshed it on the fire, ran to refill the bucket, ran back to the shed, took a second look at the fire which was now kindling the dynamite, dropped the bucket and took to his heels, screaming: "Run for your lives, the powder shanty is on fire!"

He had made scarcely forty feet when the dynamite went off with a colossal explosion. The blast dislodged fixtures, shook loose plaster and shattered windows in every building in the neighborhood. The Manhattan Eye and Ear Hospital was too damaged to receive patients, the Grand Union Hotel was a shambles and the clocks in the tower of Grand Central Station were blown in. The Murray Hill Hotel looked as if it had survived a bombardment. There was a twenty-by-15-foot hole in the street where none had been before, and it was filled within inches of the top by derricks, sandbags, planking, pieces of the shanty and other debris. Some 185 people were injured, many by glass splinters, and five were killed, most of them while eating lunch in the Murray Hill Hotel across the street. Epps himself was only bruised. The embryonic subway was hardly damaged at all and repairs took only a week.

In October of the next year, in the deepest part of the subway at 195th Street and St. Nicholas Avenue, there was an even worse disaster. A tunnel, fifty feet wide and fifteen feet high was being bored through solid rock sixty feet underground. Foreman Timothy Sullivan, directing a gang of Italian immigrants, planted dynamite, cleared the tunnel, and waved okay to the detonator. From outside the mountain seemed to heave and there was deep rumbling within. When it stopped, Sullivan roared, "Come on men, back to work," and led the way inside. Thirty men followed him. A moment later there were three more blasts, and the roof of the tunnel caved in on top of them. Those who survived rushed outside, screaming or choking, nearly paralyzed with fear. In the tunnel Sullivan and nine Italians were dead or dying. For some, pinned under a boulder estimated to weigh two hundred tons, the agony was protracted. Three men hung head downward while rescuers attacked with drills the rock which crushed the lower part of their bodies. A fourth man was caught by the leg. Frantic efforts to pry up a corner of the boulder and free him failed. At last a doctor amputated the leg. He was rushed to a hospital, but died en route. The work of identifying the dead went on for days. The Italians had arrived in America only a short time before and were known only by numbers.

All of Manhattan Island is underlined with rock, but the rock is closer to the surface in some places than in others. Thus the first subway burrowed through sand in the south, and through quicksand (fine sand and blue mud eight feet deep) near 115th Street at Broadway. This was scooped out and gravel laid in its place. Sometimes, as at Lafayette Street near Canal, the subway dipped into low areas beneath the tidewater level. Then pumps had to be used, and the walls of the cut buttressed with timbers. It was largely because of these areas, too, that the subway had to be waterproofed—literally sheathed in asphalt.

As waterproofing this treatment was a complete success— that subway would have stayed dry in a deluge. It was not until after the subway began running that engineers and passengers found out that the waterproofing was impervious to air, too. On hot days temperatures in the tunnel went up and up and up, sometimes topping a hundred degrees. Body heat and friction of wheels on rails were the causes, plus the fact that no fresh air got in or fetid air out past that formidable waterproofing. Eventually ventilators were bored through, and later subways were built with a thinner sheath of asphalt.

In some areas no obstacles were encountered and construction was swift; in others the subway proceeded northward by inches. It skirted carefully past Trinity Church on lower Broadway, for instance, because the foundation of the church ended in loose sand only nine feet below the surface. The subway at that point was deeper, twenty-four feet down, and diggers could gaze up at the massive bulk of the church as it towered above them, built on what was, in effect, nothing more solid than a sand dune. If the sand caved in, the church would land on top of them.

Again, at Columbus Circle, the subway wormed through supports of the seventy-five-foot Columbus Monument. The masonry base had to be shored up most carefully. A building, under such circumstances, could settle at one corner or another and still be repaired later. But permit the slender, fragile column of the monument to tilt and Columbus was likely to land on his head.

In places the new subway dipped beneath the rivers which rim Manhattan, to come up again in Brooklyn. The building of the river tunnels produced two almost incredible accidents. The first occurred in 1905 in the Battery-Joralemon Street tunnel. The tunneling shield had just been driven forward to a point approximating mid-river, but thirty feet below the river's bed, when, with a great hiss, the compressed air began to escape through a blowout in the roof. The procedure, carefully drilled into the workers, was to heave sandbags, which were always on hand for that purpose, into the vortex and thus plug the leak. Now, as the noise of the leak reached a fantastic pitch, a worker named Dick Creedon grabbed a bag, raced to the danger spot and started to swing the bag into place. Before he had a chance to let go of the sandbag, he and it were sucked up through thirty feet of river bed, up, up through the river itself.

Some place along the line Creedon felt the bag torn from his hands. He reached the surface dazed but swimming. A boat soon picked him up. He could not understand what had happened to him.

The break was repaired by dumping tons of sand from scows which were floated out and held in place directly over the leak.

Eleven years later, as the Whitehall-Montague tunnel of the BMT line was being built, the same thing happened. Four men were working in the tunnel when there was a fierce whistling, then a rush of air as before. Three of the four men were sucked into the vortex. One, Marshall Mabey, was swirled up through twelve feet of sand and shot to the surface on top of a geyser which eyewitnesses declared rose forty feet into the air with Mabey on top of it. When he tumbled into the river again he began swimming and a boat from the contractor's dock picked him up. His two pals were less lucky. One was not found for forty minutes, though the boat searched for him, and by that time he was dead from drowning. The other was dead before he reached the surface. His head had collided with something solid in the river bed as he shot through.

This break was repaired by dumping a blanket of clay on top of it.

In human life the cost of the first subway, and of the BMT line which followed it during the second decade of the century, was terribly high. In 1906 four Negroes were killed when a fire set off a blast causing a cave-in which buried them in a pocket in the earth. Miraculously, their ventilating column remained clear, and they must have been able to smell the fire as they waited to be rescued. Then the fire spread to a load of rubber near by, and soon there was no air at all coming down the column, just lethal fumes. All the men were dead when the diggers got to them.

In 1913 there was a cave-in at Lexington Avenue near Fifty-sixth Street, and eleven men were buried under hundred of tons of sandstone. The Italian Consul came around to help identify the dead, and the Hungarian Consul stopped by long enough to assure himself that there were no Hungarians among them. The newspapers of the day seemed to take these trage-

dies with relative calm. After all, few Americans were involved.
Immigrant laborers were expendable.

Not until 1915, when the IRT had been running ten years
and the BMT was almost finished, did the public really feel
the price of the new subways, the price of progress. At 8:22
AM on September 22 of that year, a blast was fired in the north
heading of the BMT excavation just south of Twenty-fifth
Street, the partially finished tunnel being decked over, the
deck supported by timbers, the trolley tracks running thirty
inches above the roof of the tunnel.

With the blast the deck surface seemed to rise, then sag.
Underneath, tons of rock had poured out of the wall, tumbling
against the timbers, smashing some, dislodging others. Ever
so slowly, the street above began to sink into the tunnel. Now
it happened that a loaded trolley was heading north on Seventh
Avenue at the time. The street simply opened in front of it
and still on its rails, it began to run downhill into the tunnel.
Faster and faster it ran, then jumped its track and pitched
with a fearful crash into the hole. Five workmen below looked
up into descending death. There was nothing they could do.
The trolley car crushed them.

The trolley, made of wood, was a total wreck, but only three
of its passengers died; all of them killed in the panic which
followed. A brewery truck followed it downhill into the hole,
the truck driver being among the dozens who were injured.
An improvised hospital was set up on the spot. Police, firemen
and amateur rescuers slid down ropes and sent the dazed and
injured up in litters. A twenty-four-inch gas main had broken.
Gas fumes were everywhere and all were terrified by the possibility of a gas explosion. Even so, curious thousands braved
that possibility to peer into the hole.

Within an hour, seven different investigations were under
way, and somebody set up a cry for the workman who had set
the blast. His name was August Midnight—at least that was
the name he had taken upon receiving his citizenship papers
some years before—and he had taken to his heels as soon as
he had seen the street collapse and the trolley careen into the
tunnel. Two days later he turned up voluntarily, with a lawyer.
In Italian and broken English he explained that he had pan-

icked, had run up Seventh Avenue all the way to Fifty-fourth where a relative lived. He said he had never had an accident before, but that now he did not want to work with dynamite ever again.

For the better part of thirteen years New Yorkers had walked fearlessly about on top of the decked-over subway; but now their confidence was shaken. The street had collapsed all the way to Twenty-third Street—two blocks—apparently because each dislodged timber had in turn knocked down the one in front of it. To a worried city it appeared that such accidents might become common.

Three days later it happened again, justifying popular fears. At Broadway, just north of Thirty-eighth Street, seventy-five feet of street collapsed. A fault in the rock wall of the excavation caused a small landslide, which knocked down timbers one by one. Without the support of the timbers the heavy street planking with trolley tracks on top began to sag. Again it happened very slowly, and again a loaded trolley car approached the spot at precisely the wrong moment.

But this time the motorman, Malachi Murphy, reacted swiftly. As his car began to slide into the dip, Murphy threw the machinery into reverse. For agonizing moments the car skidded toward disaster. Then the wheels took hold and the car backed slowly, then swiftly away. There was no panic on board. Nobody except Murphy realized what was happening until it was all over. He later was cited by the trolley company and rewarded.

Cab driver George Sommerer was as lucky. He had just pulled up at a cab stand, and decided to get out and stretch his legs while waiting for the next fare. He walked across the pavement to the building line and, out of the light wind which was blowing, lit a cigarette. At that moment there was a rattle of timbers—pitifully little warning, considering what was about to happen. Sommerer glanced up. A man and woman were crossing the street. Then the street opened beneath them and they simply dropped, almost without a sound, into the tunnel. Now there was a rending and tearing noise. As Sommerer watched, aghast, his cab suddenly disappeared, swallowed by the earth.

As rescuers ran up, Sommerer stammered out what had happened. He was so shocked he could scarcely talk. A doctor went down into the hole on a rope, and the woman was hauled to the surface. She was stout, wearing a new dress, and she was dead.

Astoundingly, this was the evening's only casualty. Somehow the man was only bruised. The accident happened just after seven o'clock on a Saturday evening. Office workers had long since gone home and the strollers had not yet appeared. The streets had been almost deserted.

On that crisp, October afternoon in 1904 when the first subway was opened to the public for the first time, the whole city joined in the celebration. Church bells rang out all day long, whistles screeched, new-fangled automobiles pumped their klaxons and, in the harbor, craft from tugs to ocean liners boomed their foghorns. There were flags and bunting everywhere, and you would have thought a war had ended. To the people of New York it seemed a miracle that at last the subway was here. Few knew or cared that it had first been proposed by Willson forty years before, that the Beach tube had lain rotting beneath their feet for thirty-four years, that by now many other cities had subways too, including London, Glasgow, Boston, Paris and even Budapest. *Their* subway was here, now, today. They waited with mounting anticipation to see what it would be like.

Ceremonies commenced at one o'clock in the Aldermanic Chamber at City Hall, where the Mayor, George B. McClellan, greeted a dozen politicians, churchmen, builders Belmont and McDonald, and other dignitaries. Although technically outranked by Catholic Archbishop Farley, Protestant Bishop Greer gave the blessing, which was followed by an hour and twenty-four minutes of speeches. Outside the city seemed to have gone mad with excitement. But inside, each new speech was a masterpiece of solemnity.

"We are here today for the purpose of turning over a new page in the history of New York," boomed one dignitary ponderously, trying to make himself heard above the noise in the streets.

Another got up and agitated for laws to force the utility companies to run their wires and mains in galleries inside the new subway.

At last Archbishop Farley gave a closing benediction, Mr. Belmont presented the Mayor with a mahogany case containing an ornamented silver controller—a sort of motorman's ignition key to the subway engine—and the Mayor waved it aloft crying, "I now, as Mayor, in the name of the people, declare the subway open."

Then he led the procession outside and down the steps of City Hall toward the subway entrance, bearing the ornamented controller like a sacred offering. Crowds, estimated at more than ten thousand and held back by police lines, let out a thunderous roar of approval, surged forward and burst past the men in blue. The noise of the tolling bells, hooting klaxons, whistles and foghorns seemed, if anything, louder than ever.

Downstairs into the kiosk the Mayor led his faithful followers, now swelled by several thousands. The first train was there, standing in the station, five wooden cars sheathed in bright copper, the tops painted a flaming Tuscan red. There were no doors in the sides. Entrance was via the platforms at either end. Each car sat fifty-six, and the builders had modestly named the first two of them the "Belmont" and the "McDonald"—after themselves.

Into the first car hiked the Mayor, a picture of dignity. He took his place in the motorman's closet and inserted the ornamented controller. Behind him dignitaries fought with the mob for position. According to a witness this resulted in "indescribable scenes of crowding and confusion . . . men fought, kicked and pummelled one another . . . women were dragged out either screaming in hysterics or in a swooning condition."

Another wrote that "a common spectacle all over the subway was of two persons attempting to crowd into a car door at the same time, to become wedged together, neither able to move in or out."

In the motorman's cab the Mayor was like a boy with a new toy. At his elbow, one hand on the brake, the other on the horn, stood a man who had already driven the subway and knew that its power was nothing to trifle with, the line's uneasy general manager Frank Hadley.

And so, when all were on board who could cram their way in, New York's first subway train whirled out of City Hall Station under the guiding hand of the Mayor.

A moment later it jerked to a halt—the controller had come loose. It was indubitably ornamental, silver and handsome, but a poor fit, and Mayor McCellan had his hands full trying to hold it in the wide-open position, that being the speed he preferred.

"Have you had enough, sir?" asked Hadley nervously.

"I'm running this train," responded the Mayor.

Whatever the comic aspects, it was a glorious day for New York. When the train burst momentarily into the sunlight at the short viaduct over what was then known as Manhattan Valley (West 125th Street) the hillsides were dense with people who cheered and clapped and laughed with delight to see it. All the factories had given their workers a half-holiday. As the train appeared the factory whistles blared and the hillsides were a mass of waving hands and handkerchiefs.

At top speed, rushing past station after station, it took just twenty-six minutes to reach the end of the line, which then had been completed only to 145th Street. There the Mayor pocketed his ill-fitting, silver controller, turned the train over to Mr. Hadley and faced reporters.

No, he had no difficulties to speak of, he told them modestly, crediting the fact that he had recently learned to drive "one of those automobiles," for his ease in handling the heavy train. One thing did bother him, having to hold the lever down all the way. "A precaution," Hadley pointed out hastily, "in case the motorman should die on the job."

"Splendid idea," agreed the Mayor.

The trip back to City Hall, during which the train stopped at every station, each of them now packed with people, took forty-one minutes, after which the Mayor and his party disembarked and the subway was given over to the common man. For the rest of the afternoon anyone who wanted to could ride free—and thousands upon thousands took advantage of the bargain. As each train sped uptown the seats were not only full but more than fifty persons per car were "hanging by the straps or standing in the middle tossed this way and that." For probably the first and only time in its existence, the subway carried joyriders, not irritable commuters. No one minded the terrible overcrowding, the heat or the jostling. The subway was filled with laughter and gaiety. It was a historic day, a magnificent day, and the subway was a thunderous rolling party.

The spirit was contagious. Only the stiff or the snooty were immune to it, plus the young woman whose leg was broken when she was pushed into the space between the car and the platform, and the man, one Henry Barrett, who became the first victim of subway pickpockets—some lightfingered individual made off with a $500 diamond stickpin out of his tie.

One or two soul searchers on board, anticipating television by almost half a century, asked themselves what the subway would mean to the reading habits of the city. The subway was so fast there would be scarcely time to read the paper any more. Besides, the yellow lights of the train, rushing past the white pillars of the stations, was sure to cause a new kind of eye disease. Others protested against the garish advertising posters which had been permitted to "litter the stations." It was outrageous that public transportation should submit to the crass exploitation of the advertising world. A man didn't want to be sold things during off hours while traveling to and from work.

As each passenger entered the subway, he was handed a timetable—that is, he was handed a pamphlet which included a timetable. On the cover of the pamphlet-timetable one read in gigantic letters: *SUBWAY AIR AS PURE AS YOUR OWN HOME.* Inside was another headline: *35 MILLION CUBIC FEET OF AIR SPACE,* followed by a treatise on the subject, together with the results of a survey, by a University of Columbia scientist, Professor C. F. Chandler.

This seemed to satisfy most riders. A few went around sniffing disdainfully, and one, returning into the forty-six degree autumn afternoon, felt constrained to write: "The air was so crisp and clear on the surface that by contrast the atmosphere in the tunnel seemed warm and somewhat muggy. On entering

the kiosk and taking the first few steps down, one was struck
in the face by a warm blast of air of a peculiar and none too
pleasant odor." Timetables, of course, have long since passed
out of existence, but subway air has not changed a bit.

However, these were minor complaints in a day which was
one of the happiest in the entire history of the city. Just after
six in the evening, a fuse blew and the subway was stalled for
the first time—in the tunnel near Ninety-sixth Street. Nobody
saw anything ominous in that, nor predicted that the subway
would often break down in years to come. There was apparently no fidgeting or cursing aboard the packed train, although
it took twenty minutes for another train to make the journey
up from City Hall to push its dead brother to the end of the
line. Instead people gossiped or sang or told jokes, and the
twenty minutes seemed to pass very quickly.

All day and into the night the noise, the excitement went
on, and thousands of people piled into train after train. The
confusion in the subway was monumental. People were rushing
in all directions, none of them going anywhere, just riding.
Most, on reaching the end of the line, merely crossed over
and started down—or up—on the other side. Hundreds sailed
blithely past the station where they had intended to get off,
for no one was accustomed to the rather small station name-
plates, nor knew where to look for them, and there were no
familiar landmarks visible outside to warn the traveler that
his stop was approaching, just a dark cavern filled with endless
iron pillars.

All 2,300 employees of the IRT System served at one time
or another during the day, and they must have watched aghast
as each new avalanche of riders descended upon them. Was
it going to be like this every day? On and on the people came,
the rich, the poor, the old, the young, the excited, the sophisticated, the curious and the criminal.

"The thing that seemed to be demonstrated most clearly
by the evening's experience," wrote one journalist, "was the
subway's astonishing power of digestion."

Then, as now, that's a pretty apt description of the subway.

The years wrought many changes in the subway. Not only

the timetables went, but the special reserved cars marked *LA-DIES ONLY* (that status being assured by a husky attendant guarding the door at either end) and the Tuscan red color. The ladies, it seemed, did not want to be separated from the men at all, and the segregated car was so often empty that the guards used it as a smoker. As for the Tuscan red color, all agreed that it was handsome, but it was painted over to olive drab because, according to Norman Litchfield, an early engineer of car equipment, that color "more nearly approximated the color of the dirt which accumulated on the cars no matter what color they were painted."

The IRT was finished by March, 1906. The so-called dual contracts were signed in March, 1913, bringing the BMT into the subway system. The IND line, still sometimes referred to by older New Yorkers as the "new" subway, was completed during the thirties. Various arms of the subway are still being pushed forward in some areas.

The subways remained privately owned until June of 1940, when the city bought them for $1,650,000,000. Control has since passed from the city to a city-state commission, although often it seems that the real owner of the subway is an Irish-born, lilting-voiced labor leader named Mike Quill, boss since 1936 of the Transport Workers' Union, which includes some forty thousand subway workers.

Fares have changed too. Fares were a nickel under private ownership, jumping to a dime shortly after the city took over, and to fifteen cents under the city-state. During most of that time the subway claimed to be running in the red, but profits during 1956 and 1957 were about $4,000,000.

Since 1904 subways have been delayed by fire and flood, murder and suicide, by a flock of migrating birds, by a stray dog which loped ahead of a train at three miles per hour (stopping every now and then to rest) while passengers laughed and cheered him on with cries of "Giddyap Fido!"; and even by a fat man carrying three boxes of eggs. The fat man, unable to follow his wife into the crowded car for fear that the doors would snap shut on the eggs, decided to follow on foot, sucking in his substantial gut and scrunching up tight against the wall every time a new train roared by him in the tunnel. He made it to the next station, too.

The subway has come far since thousands sat on the Manhattan Valley hillsides cheering the first train, since the night Henry Barrett lost his diamond stickpin. Nowadays everyone professes to loathe the subway, and a public relations staff has been hired to try to sell the joys of underground travel to people who, in general, want no part of it. And there is now a Transit Authority police force numbering some nine hundred men, who chase down about four thousand assorted thieves, muggers, vandals, *et. al.* a year, plus innumerable smokers, litterers and spitters.

But that day in 1904 is still a glorious one in New York City history and, when its anniversary came round exactly fifty years later, Thomas E. Dewey being Governor of the state and Robert F. Wagner being Mayor, a gala birthday celebration was planned.

The Mayor was to be there, and the members of the Downtown Manhattan Association, the Transit Authority board and many other dignitaries—as many, it seemed, as had attended the first celebration in 1904. Speeches were planned, together with flag waving, whistle tooting and an exhibition of early subway paraphernalia in a near-by museum.

Then union boss Quill, uninvited as usual, heard about the plans and demanded "time to be heard."

There would be no celebration; there could never have been a subway, he declared, were it not for "my" forty thousand men.

All Quill wanted was the opportunity to make a speech. But Quill's speeches are always the same, delivered in a lilting County Kerry brogue, and highly vituperative. No one ever willingly gives him the opportunity to make one.

In this case there was furious back-pedaling by all concerned. "We can't invite him," disclaimed the Transit Authority. "It's not our party."

"I'm only an invited guest myself," said John D. Butt, President of the Downtown Manhattan Association.

"New York City is no longer in the subway business," said

Mayor Wagner. "I never said I'd come to this meeting in the first place."

A day or so later the Mayor's secretary announced that the Mayor regretted he would be unable to attend. Next workmen were sent out to dismantle the platform which had been erected on the City Hall steps.

October 27, 1954, dawned bright and clear. Mr. Butt and some lesser dignitaries were present, but the celebration would have been a complete dud, had it not been for Quill. He had sent a hundred pickets. Round and round the building they paraded, bearing signs which read:

> *FARES UP, SERVICE DOWN*
> *MAKES NEW YORK A ONE HORSE TOWN*

Also:

> *IF SUBWAY SERVICE IS PHOOEY*
> *DON'T CALL WAGNER, BLAME DEWEY.*

Across the street, a statue of Nathan Hale in chains brooded silently.

Quill himself arrived aboard a hundred-year-old red-and-yellow "tally-ho" wagon pulled by two not-quite-white horses driven by Hopalong Abramowitz of the Bronx. This ancient vehicle, according to a placard, represented fifty years of subway progress. *THIS IS YOUR SUBWAY SERVICE IN '55*, blared a second placard.

"My men have certain grievances," orated Quill. The neighboring fire brigade roared out of its shed to answer an alarm, drowning him out.

"This is a birthday party," said Mr. Butt when his turn came to speak, "not a report of fifty years' progress."

The "glorious," "wondrous" New York subway was half a century old.

9. "Smelly" Kelly, Subway Sniffer

NOT LONG AGO a tavern owner on Sixth Avenue, beside himself with rage, telephoned the Transit Authority.

"You should smell my place," he fumed. "Somethin's leaking in here from the subway. It stinks so bad ya gotta wear a gas mask. I got no business left. I'm suing you, you hear me. I'm suing you for everything you got!"

"Don't be hasty," cried the Transit official. "The best man we have is on his way over there right now."

Mollified, the tavern owner growled: "What's his name?"

"Smelly Kelly."

"What? Don't kid me!"

"He's the best in the business. Smelly Kelly."

"You blankety-blank wise guy. I'll sue you for everything you've got."

Smelly Kelly, also known as Leaky or Sniffy, is in charge of leaks in the subway. He has found thousands of them. So uncanny is his sense of smell, his delicate nostrils, that he is renowned the length and breath of the subway system.

But his fame had not permeated as far as the Sixth Avenue tavern, whose owner did not believe that such a person did or could exist. However, the stench in the place was overpowering. Only a few old-timers continued to brave it, and the owner was willing to try anything.

All turned from the bar as Kelly strode imperiously through the door.

"Kelly," the newcomer announced.

"Smelly Kelly?" asked the owner dubiously.

"The same."

Kelly removed his hat, his coat.

"Also known as Leaky or Sniffy," Kelly said proudly. Without further ado, he hoisted his famous nose into the air and sniffed tentatively. It was like an athlete warming up, shaking the kinks out of a muscle.

Then Smelly got down to serious business. Pointing his proboscis this way and that, he sniffed powerfully.

Smelly's nostrils began to twitch. He had fastened on a scent.

Impressed, despite himself, the tavern owner asked: "What do you think?"

A breathless hush had come over the tavern.

"Rats!" announced Mr. Kelly.

He moved in ever-diminishing circles, sniffing expertly.

"Rats," Smelly said again.

He stood upon a chair to sniff the ceiling, then tapped it with his fist.

"Rats," he said. "And they're in there."

His audience, under the spell of the artist at work, stared at him, mesmerized.

Then the owner cried: "You heard the man, boys."

The ceiling was attacked from all sides, with all manner of weapons. In a moment a section of it came away. Out slid the decomposing corpses of a tribe of rats who, having partaken of rat poison, had crawled into the ceiling to die.

"It wasn't the subway at all," said the owner, gazing at Smelly in awe.

Kelly accepted congratulations modestly. "So many smells do come from the subway that it takes a lot of experience to pick out the ones that don't," he said.

For thirty-three years it has been Smelly's job to patrol the tracks of the IND Division of the New York Subway System (about three hundred miles of track) searching out sagging pavement, stained walls, strange odors, shifting rock or soil, sudden pools of water—all of which mean leaks. At times Kelly has also been responsible for strange-smelling parcels left in stations, varnish or paint too close to third rails, subterranean rivers as old as Manhattan itself, and dogs, cats, mice and other rodents and even fish which have somehow become entangled in the intricate workings of the subway.

So dependent upon Kelly did the city become that a new title was contrived to describe his job—he was named the first and only Superintendent of Subway Structures—and he was assigned to head a staff of six assistant smellers.

By now Smelly and his nose are legendary.

"The guy is like a bird dog," says one incredulous admirer. "Put him near a leak and he points."

If the New York Subway System has never had a significant explosion or cave-in, part of the reason is Smelly. He has hiked all seven hundred twenty miles of track in his time, averaging about ten miles a day for a career-total of nearly one hundred thousand miles—sniffing rhythmically every step of the way. Requirements for detecting leaks? "Quick ears, good nose, better feet," says Kelly, who always talks as if dictating a report.

The average find is eight leaks a day, some of them deadly serious. "Some awfully dangerous stuff drips down from the streets," says Kelly. "It may take a week for the liquid to seep down on tunnel ceiling. And you would see the stain too late. Once the fumes get a start, all you need is a single spark off the third rail. . . .

"Leaking gas is never in one place long enough to figure it," Smelly goes on. "So you've got to figure the leak before it figures you and blows everything to kingdom come."

And he adds, "If I don't want a train to run after I take a sniff, she don't run."

Once Kelly answered a complaint about a midtown subway station which smelled like tar.

"That's what gasoline fumes smell like underground," said Smelly, sniffing. Having identified the fumes by nose, he measured them with an instrument the size of a lunch box called an explosimeter. The meter showed a concentration of eight points, twenty less than certain explosion.

What did he do?

"Evacuated station, called fire department."

Teddy May, "The King of the Sewers," worked underground for fifty-one years.

Kelly and his nose are legendary.

Huge ventilators were opened at points above and below the pocket of gas. While Kelly laboriously traced the fumes to the leaky storage reservoir of a nearby gas station, southbound trains were ordered to coast down the incline past the station with motors cut, to prevent possible sparks from setting off the explosion. Northbound trains were ordered to "proceed cautiously."

It was ten and a half hours before Kelly gave the all clear.

Another time, Smelly was called to the Forty-second Street IND station. The platforms were permeated by a stench so powerful it nearly knocked him down. He couldn't believe his nose.

"For a moment I thought my smelling days were over," said Smelly. Then he got a grip on himself and began to sniff.

"It smells like elephants," he mused. The more he sniffed the more convinced he became that that's what it was.

His skeptical superiors, reading his report, became convinced that Kelly had slipped his trolley for good. Elephants in the subway? Impossible.

But Smelly persisted, and at length discovered that the subway station lay directly under the site of the old Hippodrome, where a herd of elephants had once trumpeted on the stage. A water main had burst, soaking long-buried elephant dung and driving the fumes into the station.

Kelly will back his nose against any man's, but not against scientific instruments. He uses several on the job, some of them of his own invention.

One is his privately designed aquaphone. This he invented in a subway workshop. It is simply an antique telephone receiver with a hollow rod soldered to the diaphragm. When he suspects a leak he touches this device to the nearest fire hydrant. Through it he can hear a hissing noise, which tells him that the leak is near.

With this information in hand, he might next employ his stethoscope. This is not a common, garden-variety, doctor's model. Again Smelly has soldered a rod to the diaphragm. He bends toward the sidewalk, the plugs in his ears, the rod pointed down. As carefully as a physician probes the chest of a patient, Smelly probes the chest of the city. Inside the chest all manner of rumbling is going on. Trains thunder along, tools ring against pipes and—the noise is faint, but Smelly's ear, trained as acutely as his famous nose, picks it out of the meaningless jangle—the hissing of a broken main.

Kelly casts about until he determines the direction of the break, then closes in on it. Finally through the earpieces of his hypersensitive stethoscope, he can hear the leak directly below. The leak has been found. His job is done.

Some of his tools are more primitive, a map of the city dated 1793, for instance, or a book of ordinary matches. He uses the map to locate sub-surface streams and springs which still burble on, causing trouble, though weighted by the entire city. The matches are for "flash tests."

Smelly explains: "At Canal Street a barrel of some chemical used for making plastic combs rolled off a truck and broke. The chemical poured down a sewer, and soon people going by on the subway began to complain about a bad odor clinging to their clothes. We got a sample of the fluid and touched a match to it. It exploded. That's the flash test. When you get a positive flash test you call the fire department."

Smelly knows nothing about chemistry, but his nose knows. He claims that his proclivities in that direction are inherited. Born James Patrick Kelly in Ireland near the borders of Counties Kilkenny and Waterford in 1898, he began sniffing at sixteen.

"My uncle was a well digger by trade," he recalls. "He used a divining rod to locate water. I take after him. Always made a hobby of it."

Kelly left Ireland at eighteen and served in the British Navy during the first war, manning hydraphones on an anti-submarine vessel. When war ended he came to America and found work as a carpenter, descending into the subways for a private contractor as part of a track maintenance force. In 1926 he joined the Transit Authority as a maintenance engineer.

By 1932 he had acquired a certain reputation for finding leaks no one else even suspected, and he was challenged by a chief engineer to discover one which was plaguing the Hotel New Yorker. The entire hotel was beginning to stink. Downstairs there was a telltale stained wall, but, short of ripping the whole wall out, none among the army of engineers consulted could devise a method of pinpointing the break.

Kelly was led to the site where, after a moment's study, he announced: "I should be able to find that."

"How long will it take you?"

"Half an hour."

To paraphrase the well-known piano advertisement, they laughed when Kelly sat down at the plumbing. From his pocket he withdrew a packet of uranine, a yellow powder which was then little known. Kelly's formal education is scant, but his ingenuity is formidable and he had once noted somewhere that a pound of uranine would color a million gallons of water.

So he introduced the yellow powder into the plumbing and began to flush. Before the allotted half hour had expired, a small yellow blush had begun to tint the wall in question. That's where a broken pipe joint was found, and the Hotel New Yorker's B.O. problem was solved.

"After that," says Smelly, "I was in leaks for keeps."

During World War II, uranine was standard equipment in flyers' survival kits, and many men forced down at sea owe their lives to the stain, visible to searching planes, which it spread on the surface of the sea. There are several authorities who credit Smelly Kelly with first demonstrating that the chemical could be used for this purpose.

Now sixty-two, the subway's sniffing sleuth is husky, gray-haired, of medium height and nose. In his long career he has known both victory and defeat.

A notable victory occurred when he was called to a subway washroom to discover why there was no water pressure in the taps. Several plumbers had already admitted that they could find no leaky or broken main.

"Of course not," said Kelly, after making a check with his aquaphone. "I'll show you what the trouble is. Remove the faucets."

This was done, the impatient plumbers indicating by their manner that they considered Kelly a meddling fool.

The taps removed, Kelly began to work a probe down into the pipe. In a few moments he slowly withdrew the instrument with great care and deliberation.

"What are you doing?" demanded one of the plumbers.

"Fishing," said Smelly.

Out came the probe. Attached to it dangled a two-and-a-half-foot eel.

"They always laugh at me when I say it's a fish causing the trouble," said Kelly when recounting this story. "It's no laughing matter. I've also caught forty killifish and a ten-inch trout. Same are always dead when caught."

One of Kelly's most interesting defeats also occurred in a subway washroom. A steam line had burst and was sloshing live steam against a water pipe connected to the Forty-second Street men's room. Kelly found the break all right, but not before the department had received a number of heated complaints about toilets which flushed steam.

Since Smelly's job requires him to follow his nose along subway tracks, he often faces real danger. Once the end of a length of wire he was carrying dropped against the 660 volts of the third rail. The jolt knocked him down. He got up, made certain that he had a better grip on the wire this time, and calmly continued on his way.

In the summer of 1939, Kelly and his crew were doing some cement grouting work (pouring cement under the tracks to bolster the track foundation) a block north of the 103rd Street IND Station. As a northbound express came through, the men stepped between the massive support columns that separate the uptown tracks from the downtown tracks. These columns are about five feet apart and about three feet wide.

In the slot just down from Kelly was Anthony Bauman. As the second car of the nine-car train started by, Kelly noticed Bauman slumping forward. The third car slapped him.

"He must have gotten train-shy, the way you get gun-shy," reported Kelly afterwards.

Instantly, Kelly flattened himself against the train side of the giant pillar and side-stepped across to Bauman's niche, grabbing the sinking man underneath the arms and holding him until the ninth car went by.

It was a big risk to take. Only inches separated Kelly's chest from the onrushing train as he slipped along the outside of the pillar to get to Bauman. Bauman was six feet tall and weighed two hundred pounds. Kelly is five feet nine, 165. If Kelly hadn't caught him, he would have fallen underneath the train and been killed. And if the man had slipped one foot while in Kelly's grasp, he would have touched the third rail and both men would have been toasted by the 660 volts.

"A big man," recalls Kelly, "but I held him up while the train went by. Held him for thirty seconds. Same felt like thirty years."

For his heroism, Kelly won his first of two Board commendations, which go only to men who have risked their lives in the performance of duty.

The second was won four years later. A man jumped or fell onto the tracks at 103rd Street and Central Park West, just as a train was approaching. Kelly happened to be riding in the first car. The motorman tried to stop, but the first car ran over the man, who fortunately was lying unconscious in the trough between the tracks. No one knew what to do until Kelly volunteered to crawl under the train and lie on top of the man while the train was backed off.

So Kelly took off his coat, crawled under the train and signaled with his flashlight that he had the man pinned down. If the man had struggled while the train was moving, both he and Kelly might have been killed.

In his time, Kelly has broken in fifty or sixty qualified smellers, who have spread out into all corners of the subway system. He says it takes at least a year before you can trust a new man on the job, and complains that most new men aren't interested enough, so you can't have confidence in them.

What Kelly is saying in essence is that there are others who try, or have tried, but there's only one Smelly Kelly. Asked about the six men in his own crew he has said. "Good men, all of them, but—" There the sentence trails off, but the inference is clear. To these men sniffing is merely a job. They don't seem to grasp the tremendous significance of the art.

However, Charles L. Patterson, present Chairman of the Transit Authority, concurs in Smelly's modest estimate of himself. "In thirty years in the railroad business," according to Mr. Patterson, "I have never before encountered a man with the peculiar talents of Mr. Kelly."

And Kelly's immediate superior, Assistant Superintendent Schlager, has said: "It will be a sad day for us when Smelly retires."

At sixty-two, Smelly has finally begun to take it easy. He now works the eight-to-four shift whenever possible, and leaves most of the walking to younger men. He is still on emergency call twenty-four hours a day, however.

The job of subway sniffing has not changed much over the years. "Mostly you walk," says Kelly. "You make regular inspection trips beneath gasoline storage tanks of service stations, beneath raw chemical factories, beneath storage areas for manufactured gas. You check areas known to form pockets of sewer gas, and areas beneath new construction jobs where a steam shovel might scrape gas mains. Sometimes a guy calls in and says he smelled something on a certain train which made him dizzy. You intercept the train and find some guy sitting in the corner with a ten-gallon jug of gasoline. You get characters like that up into the street fast. You'd be surprised how many people think nothing of riding the subways with explosive liquids."

If Smelly Kelly did not exist he would have to be invented. For there will always be leaks in the subways, water leaks which could cause cave-ins, seeping fumes which build into pockets of gas waiting only for a spark for the next onrushing express. Leaking gas means explosion, fire, destruction, death to many persons. Only a Smelly Kelly, following his nose along the track, can find, identify and obviate fumes before they attain lethal concentrations.

His only known competitors are a pair of bloodhounds who have been trained by the Natural Gas Odorizing Company of Houston, Texas, to recognize the odor of a leaking gas main. Smelly is confident that dogs will never replace him.

"Dogs," says Smelly Kelly stiffly, "are not allowed in the subway."

10. Nine Miles of Gas

SECOND ONLY TO WATER in burrowing beneath the streets of the city were the slender, cast-iron mains of the New York Gas Light Company.

For a time there was doubt that the new gas mains would be of cast iron, or that they would ever be entrenched. The city, stung once by Burr's Manhattan Company, had become chary of offering its favors, and the original gas charter which was granted in the spring of 1823, stipulated that the company should not engage in banking or insurance, should not issue notes, bills or other negotiable paper and that, furthermore, "no public street, lane or highway shall be dug into, or in anywise injured or defaced. . . ."

For six weeks the company directors argued this out with the State Legislature and the city authorities, and at last it was agreed that the mains could go underground, provided that the company promised to "manufacture a sufficient quantity of gas for lighting the houses and public lamps in Broadway from the Battery to Grand Street"; the streets to be lighted at the company's expense.

Another clause specified that the pipes would be constructed "in the most approved manner of cast iron and of the best materials." The city wanted no more hollow logs under its streets. At this time wooden mains conducted gas in France; in England, gun barrels which littered the Continent after the Napoleonic Wars, had been screwed together to form gas pipe. The ingenious English also had used glass tubes, lead pipes

116

and pipes made of charred wood covered with animal gut coated with varnish. The inspired inventor who created the last type, never did succeed in explaining it advantages.

By this time there were seven different gas companies lighting two hundred miles of London streets and sixty thousand home fixtures. The gaslight era had reached half a dozen other English cities too, and had crossed the Channel to illuminate Paris, Brussels and Munich. In Edinburgh, the gas company chairman was Sir Walter Scott—the same Sir Walter who had, scarcely a decade before, denounced gas as a "pestilential innovation."

"A madman," he had cried incredulously, "has proposed to light London with—what do you think—with smoke!"

As early as 1812 American promoters and carnival pitchmen had used "the spirit that burns like a flame" as crowd-pulling exhibits, together with sword swallowers and six-fingered dwarfs. People came away from the gas display marveling: What would science think of next? Where would it all end?

One farsighted individual even made an attempt to slip a gas charter past the New York State Legislature. This failed. But appetite for the possibilities of gas had been whetted, and in 1816 New York City's Common Council decided to foster "arts and sciences and . . . useful inventions." A committee was appointed to study the subject of gaslight. Within a few weeks a furnace and gasometer had been constructed in an old building near City Hall, and temporary tin pipes had been jointed together alongside the curbs of Chatham Street and Broadway as far as Fulton. There was just enough pressure in the tin mains to light a few street lamps, one or two store windows, and Tammany Hall. According to the *National Advocate*, the light was "presented in elegant gilt figures, and exhibited in different forms, arranged with taste and judgment, without smell, smoke, want of attendance or danger of conflagration."

Then in 1823, the New York Gas Light Company appointed a manager, awarded him the magnificent salary of $1,000 per annum, and dispatched him, via the fastest sailing vessel of the time, to England. His duty was to observe the gasworks there, to buy all necessary equipment and gear, including mains, and return as swiftly as possible to New York. The manager, one Timothy Dewey, did not come back for seven and a half months, having tarried not only in London, but in Paris too— strictly to observe the Paris gasworks, of course.

There was an even longer wait for the mains which Dewey had ordered, and the company, to keep itself in the public eye, staged a number of "expositions." That is, it set up some burners in a hall and invited the blue bloods of the day to come in and be amazed by the brilliance of the new light. For the common people, a single lamppost was planted in Franklin Square, in front of a bank, which flickered and flared through the night. This lamppost completely enthralled after-dinner strollers, and possibly it even scared away a bank robber or two. For who would consider robbing a bank when the gaslight lamppost had "torn asunder the mantle of night and turned darkness into day"?

Through the summer and autumn of 1824 the work of building the first plant and laying the first street mains went steadily forward, and it was even noted in the press that the "Pipes, imported, have been found on trial to be perfectly tight."

At the Gas Company office, Dewey sat behind a desk accepting orders for the new service and recounting his experiences in Paris.

While Broadway waited for the gas street lights which would first bring it fame as "The Great White Way," the newspapers cursed and denounced the oil lamps of the day: "Our streets last evening were so dimly lighted that it seemed as if they were mourning for the loss of the moon. We think a reward might have been safely offered to any person standing at the Coffee House that could count the lamps on either side of Wall Street to William Street. Five and twenty full grown lightning bugs would have stared them out of all countenance."

For all that, facilities were better than they had ever been before. Prior to 1697, the only lighting in the streets of New York were the lanterns carried by the night watchmen. In that year the Common Council decreed that "every 7th house . . . doe every night until the 25th of March next cause a lanthorn and candle to be hung out on a pole." It was 1762 before oil lamps were mounted on the poles, oil lamps that smoked and smelled and which, when dirty, gave hardly any light at all. On nights when a full moon was scheduled, even these lamps were not lighted. If sudden clouds obscured the moonlight, the city would be absolutely dark and thugs and hoodlums would crawl out of their holes in droves, to pounce upon careless or unlucky pedestrians.

At last on May 9, 1825, the gas company announced that it was prepared to supply gas to houses the length of Broadway. Before the summer was over it had installed seventeen hundred burners in various buildings and had so many orders on file that it could not fill them—there were simply not enough workmen.

Naturally, since the streets were to be lighted at company expense, the mains had not yet been connected to lampposts along Broadway. It would be 1828 before the demand of private consumers slackened a bit and the company could attend to that little detail.

For the moment the city was overjoyed at the new light. Shops and business began to stay open at night, their brightly lighted places attracting hordes of sight-seers, some of whom would stare and gape and then, out of pleasure or befuddlement or both, place large orders.

Other merchants and homeowners rushed to apply for the new service and before long the company was forced to issue this bulletin:

"In consequence of the unexpected consumption of gas, and daily increase of new orders, the manager has to request that those taking it will use it as sparingly as possible for a few evenings, and until the apparatus, now nearly completed for making an ample supply, is in operation. Those who have been recently fitted, and not supplied, will not have to wait longer than the middle of next week. It will be necessary to stop the supply at 11 o'clock for a few evenings."

Of course there were also those who hated gas, or feared it, or could not understand it. The powerful candle and whale-oil interests tried to crush the infant industry but failed. Bible-quoting preachers mounted their pulpits and shouted that God had appointed the day and the night and that to attempt to improve on God was blasphemous.

Pompous physicians insisted that homes were now so bright

that people would begin to keep late hours, exposing themselves to the injurious night air. Many constables claimed that
the extraordinary brightness of the new lamps would frighten
their horses—why, thieves and gangsters would get away with
murder! Prohibitionists snorted that gaslight only meant more
drinking time for weak-willed men who should be home with
their wives and children. There were even those who believed
that twilight had a calming influence which preserved men from
sin; and, with gaslight, twilight no longer existed.

The superstitious were terrified of the new invention, believing that the flames themselves ran hotly, dangerously through
the pipes. Even the scientist, Sir Humphry Davy, asserted that:
"You would have to fill St. Paul's dome to get as much gas
as you need, and then it would explode." Many, many persons
were afraid of fire, explosion, asphyxiation.

The company was also accused of contaminating well water
and of obstructing traffic when laying mains. "It is next to impossible to have a smooth and handsome street," fumed one
idealist, "as long as you suffer it to be broken up almost every
day of the year to lay down gas or water pipes."

Still, people rushed to invite the new gas pipes into their
homes. There was so much business that the company voluntarily dropped prices. In fact, business was too good, causing
the birth of a sharp new company which jumped into the ring
and began to slug it out with the old. Peace, splitting the
island into two parts, came in 1833. The New York Company
held its franchise below Canal and Grand streets, ceding the
largely uninhabited area above to the new Manhattan Gas
Light Company. When the dust had cleared and the New
York looked around, it had lost any possibility of expansion
to the north, and also its manager, Timothy Dewey. Dewey,
possibly hoping for another trip to Paris, had gone over to the
other side.

New complaints appeared in the press. "Our streets are
again in an uproar. . . . We found the Bowery lined with men
and gas pipes yesterday morning. . . . The Manhattan Gas
Light Company had commenced piping for uptown." Later
the pipes were reported as "snugly under ground."

Where the pipes were to be laid was early a matter of politics and argument. The New York Company, older, more solidly established, its territory tighter, soon had lighted all principal thoroughfares in lower Manhattan. Then it began laying pipes even in byways and alleys, a network "ever more intricate and fine."

The Manhattan Gas Light Company began at the frontier of the city, extending outward to what seemed in 1833 a vast, not-too-promising wilderness. But the population increased swiftly in the next ten years, and overcrowding, fires and plagues drove families north to the "country" in great waves. By 1843, the Manhattan was laying mains faster than the New York, though still only in the most important streets.

Petty jealousy now was rampant. Every city politician stumped to have his own particular street lighted. Alderman Carman, after falling over a hydrant one dark night, demanded that Spring Street be lighted next. Another Alderman stated decisively that obviously Fourteenth Street deserved to be piped first. Snorted Carman hotly: "Perhaps you will get somebody to live in it first, besides you."

The gas business was still in its infancy. In the plants many of the men were deathly afraid of the product they manufactured, and the chief task of the plant manager often was to coax his men to remain on the job.

"Now, boys," one of them was credited with saying, "don't run until you see me run—but when I run, you run fast, or I'll beat you to the door."

There were occasional leaks in the plants, and a large supply of whisky was kept on hand for reviving workers who passed out after inhaling quantities of gas—every time a man fell to the floor a pal would grab the whisky, pry open his mouth and start pouring. Before long it was noticed that the man who poured in the morning generally turned up as a patient in the afternoon, and vice versa. In fact, men were collapsing all over the place, even those nowhere near fumes. Whereupon, beer was substituted for whisky. The men grumbled, but went on fainting. Finally the company decided that milk would do the job just as well. After that, it was amazing how seldom men were overcome by fumes.

Whisky had another important use in the early history of

gas. The first meters were elaborate contraptions loaded with water—which tended to freeze in winter. There was no central heating to thaw them, so the gas companies came up with an ingenious solution. "Fill your meters with whisky," the consumers were advised. And the companies sent around men selling whisky for four dollars a gallon; enough whisky was bought to fill ten times the meters then in use.

Meters were unpopular from the start. The meters were attached where the pipes from street mains protruded into a man's cellar, and not one in a thousand consumers understood how they worked. Gas flowed through the street mains at the same pressure day and night. Thus the pressure at the home lamps varied according to how many other customers were also using the gas. At noon (when the sun did a satisfactory job of illumination) the lamps would blaze fiercely, there being few lighted. After dinner, when people wanted light to read by, so many consumers turned on the gas that in some areas it barely flickered, and had to be supplemented with candles. As more and more families went to bed, the gaslight fixtures would flare brightly again.

Naturally meter readings would vary according to the time of day the gas was used, and also according to how far from the plant the gas had traveled before entering the home.

Customers learned to hate the meters with a passion. "It is an insult to a respectable citizen," thundered one journalist, "to take the word of a pot-bellied object of green tin, with its expressionless face, in preference to his own, and to threaten to leave him in the dark because the thing accuses him, on its honor, of having consumed gas that he knows, and the company knows, he did not consume."

Some years later the "lying" meter also inspired this bitter —but funny—piece in the august New York *Times:*

"The plan of training small dogs to bite all persons apparently bent upon examining gas meters was originated in this city some years ago by an enterprising dog fancier. He made it his business to breed and train what he called 'gas dogs,' and was equally successful with rough-haired terriers and Spitz dogs.

"Excellent results have been attained by the use of gas dogs.

An amiable lady residing in Thirty-fifth Street, in this city, has no less than forty-three samples of trousers collected by her gas dog in the course of five years. There are now employed, either permanently or for three days in each month, fully five thousand gas dogs above the region of Bleecker Street, and we shall be safe in assuming that at least 4,500 gas inspectors are bitten either in the legs or the trousers every month.

"It need hardly be said that gas dogs are wonderfully soothing to the householder's mind. There are householders who make it a point to remain at home all day on the day when the gas inspector is expected, merely to enjoy the yell of the inspector when the gas dog's teeth go in his calf, or to listen to the inspector's language as a fresh hole is made in his trousers.

"Hundreds of our leading citizens, including clergymen and professional philanthropists, who own or employ gas dogs, have testified that they can now pay their gas bills with comparative equanimity, cheered by the recollections of the legs and trousers that the faithful gas dogs have sampled."

On another occasion the *Times* wrote:

"At a meeting of gas consumers the other night, a Mr. Van Zandt mentioned in a tone of complaint that although he had ceased to use gas at his house and had substituted for it kerosene oil, his gas bills were as large as ever.

"Many men have had Mr. Van Zandt's experience, and as a rule they have seemed to think that a gas company which sends in bills for gas that has not been consumed is dishonest. If the manufacture and sale of gas were a mere business, this view of the matter would be right, but in point of fact the manufacture and sale of gas is not a business in the ordinary sense of the term, it is a religion."

11. Cigar Stubs + Lemon Peels + Pork Fat = Gas

THREE DECADES PASSED. At mid-century, gaslighting was to be found everywhere, and the service should have achieved the status of a commonplace. It hadn't however, largely because the industry, which had learned to light the world, was itself still staggering around in the dark, bumping into things.

For instance, one afternoon in 1848 the New York Company plant took fire. "The combustion," wrote the *Post*, "formed one of the grandest . . . scenes ever witnessed in the city." It was a sad day for the company, but the city at large had never seen anything so splendid. "One immense pyramid of smoke of tartarean blackness sheathed a tower of flame which, ever and anon, showed itself through the rolling, waving, mounting mass of total darkness." It was a terrific spectacle and all of New York was agog, watching. Higher and higher mounted the great column of smoke, its color turning to purple as it met the rays of the descending sun.

The fact was that people still did not know what to expect from gas. Was it servant or master?

Hotel rooms still displayed signs under which guests were expected to slumber peacefully. The signs read: "*DANGER-OUS!* If you do not know how to turn off the gas, ask someone. Do not blow it out. It will kill you."

There was also the popular story of the country folks who loaded themselves into a wagon at the farm and drove down to the big city to visit some friends. The family which they visited, alarmed by their numbers, got rid of them for the night by claiming that a smallpox patient was in the house. The farmers went to a hotel, where all six packed into a single room. The officious old woman tucked in her sons and husband, then put her shoe over the gas jet to put it out and turned the water faucet, having heard somewhere that to put out gas a something had to be turned. In the night the porter was alarmed by smelling gas. He found the country folk all unconscious in the room and the floor flooded with water.

As late as 1854 the gas companies were still adhering to the policy laid down in 1697—they extinguished their street lights as unnecessary on moonlit nights. Down along the water front there were still no lights at all. In the darkness, safe from groping police, the city's underworld met to plan jobs, divide swag or hold kangaroo courts. Warehouses were robbed and men murdered, all in the dark. The companies, still lighting streets at their own expense, did not want to send mains under the streets near the docks because no potential private consumers lived there.

On the other hand, the companies were quick to inflate the balloons of Thaddeus Lowe and other aeronauts of the day because the fees were ample and the publicity was considered advantageous.

Lowe had an "Aeronautic Amphitheater" at the corner of Fifty-ninth Street and Sixth Avenue, an amphitheater surrounded by grandstands and posters advertising nighttime ascents: "Don't fail to see New York by Gaslight!"

One John Wise had opened a balloon factory and, in an article entitled "Systematic Ballooning" in the *American Gas-Light Journal*, had prophesied that every village in the country would one day have its own coal-gas plant, and every plant would boast facilities for inflating balloons. Why, one day a trip in a balloon would be no more remarkable than a buggy ride!

This is not to say that the companies neglected their primary business. In twenty years the New York Company had doubled its customers, tripled its mileage of mains and was supplying ten times as many street lamps, each one at a loss.

The Manhattan Company, serving an area three times larger, had twice as many customers and twice as many street lamps. It was building another plant and had begun laying double mains in many of the principal streets.

Further to the north, even the remote village of Harlem had acquired a gaslight company. It was 1855 when the first mains were buried beneath Harlem's streets. They were tiny, mostly only three-quarter-inch pipes, but they went under the sod and were connected to fixtures in the best homes in the village. The company now placed the two major orders which would permit it to do business: five hundred tons of coal from New-castle to make gas, and a horse, harness and cart which could plod about the district selling the new service and, later, col-lecting bills. The coal never arrived, because the ship carrying it sank in a storm in mid-Atlantic. But the horse lived to be twenty-four, always did his work cheerfully and, at his death, deserved a better fate than to be boiled up for glue. He should have been stuffed and enshrined in whatever gas museum might someday exist. He was a good deal more reliable than gas service from the Harlem company.

To be sure, the Harlem had special problems. Its territory was vast (it seemed then), sparsely settled and, in the laying of mains, intractable. The granite base of Manhattan, north of Harlem, is close to the surface. There are innumerable hills which, under a thin coating of turf, are solid rock. The Har-lem not only had to blast and bore many of its main-holding trenches, it also had to light hilltop streets and houses. Thus its gas pressure seemed strange and erratic. In order to make the gas flow at all to the heights along 125th Street, or in the eastern outskirts of Yorkville, it had to be driven through the mains under pressure so intense that it fairly hissed from the burners in homes close to the plant.

Neither of the other companies, blessed with flat, often sandy lower Manhattan, had faced such demands. Nor had they been obliged, as the Harlem was, to light stretches of "streets" which might more accurately have been described as country road. Some of these stretches were three-quarters of a mile in length, unpaved and totally unoccupied. The Harlem lit them nonetheless.

By the end of its first year the Harlem was servicing about
750 public lamps, roughly a quarter as many as the New York,
a tenth as many as the Manhattan. By May of 1858 the company had buried seventeen miles of mains. By the end of that
year its pipes had wormed under virgin northern Manhattan
to within three hundred feet of Spuyten Duyvil—the end of
the island—meaning that thirty miles of main were now in
existence.

This was ambition on the grand scale. The company's plant
on East 110th Street could not send gas nearly that far, a fact
which its salesmen successfully concealed when signing up new
customers. These customers soon began screaming that the
gas had all been exhausted from the mains before it ever got
to them. Some refused to pay bills for gas not received. Others
threatened to dig into the streets and rip up the company's
mains, just to get even.

Finally, in 1864, the company erected a small telescopic
gasometer at Dyckman Street and Broadway which was
equipped with an exhauster to suck the gas up from the plant,
five miles away. The laying of a great, twenty-inch main across
110th Street to Broadway also helped.

All the companies now were laying big mains. The New
York, which had started with half-inch pipes under the streets
of the lower East Side in 1825, began laying eighteen-inch
mains in 1852 and twenty-inch mains in 1859. So did the
Manhattan. It was not crowded under the streets in those
days, and no one ever thought to remove the small pipes which
would no longer be used. They are still there (so are Burr's
wooden water pipes) and are constantly being encountered
by modern diggers who, puzzled, lean on their shovels and stare
at them, not knowing what they are or to whom they belong.

The gas industry, as the Civil War struck, was solidly established but did not realize it and had no confidence. It was
constantly being scared by something or other, and each time
it jumped about frantically until the fright wore off. New competitors terrified it. So did the prospect of an imminent gas
war. So did the discovery of oil in Pennsylvania. So did every
self-styled genius who happened by, announcing the invention
of a cheaper or brighter burning gas.

One chap came round with a plan for manufacturing illuminating gas out of garbage. He had experimented, he claimed, with a cabbage leaf, a piece of bone, three cigar stubs, the butt of a cigarette, some potato peels, a snatch of leather, a dried lemon peel, a piece of pineapple rind, a banana skin, a chunk of fat pork rind, a bit of lean corned beef, eggshells, a half-eaten, mustard-daubed sandwich, a dirty rag, a bunch of beet tops, dried mint and two maggots.

This individual was patently balmy. But did the gas barons order him thrown out? Not at all. Perhaps he wasn't the madman he seemed to be. Perhaps he was actually a scientific giant. Perhaps one of the other companies would get hold of him and then . . .

The industry was constantly on the defensive. For some time people had complained earnestly about the mighty stench which rose from the gasworks. This sulphurous odor was so insupportable that, whenever a new gas plant was built, families moved away from the area in droves. Soon the gasworks seemed surrounded by desert. No one lived there anymore.

A method involving wet lime had been invented to purify the gas sent through the mains into the homes. It could be burned without odor and did not cause headaches. However, the left-over lime itself caused a new problem. The aroma which hung over it was sickening. It could (and did on at least one occasion) knock over a horse.

As New York grew more and more densely populated, complaints grew louder. Some companies invented new methods for reducing odor. At least one decided instead on a novel solution—it merely denied responsibility for the all-pervading stench which surrounded its plant.

At last the Board of Health cracked down. Its "odor detectives" succeeded, one summer day in 1868, in tracing the odor beyond any doubt to the plant's "purifying" apparatus. The company was forthwith ordered to change its purifying process or quit manufacturing gas.

Whereupon the company changed its plea from not guilty, to guilty-with-an-explanation.

Lime gases were far from unhealthy, it insisted. In fact they were actually a specific for whooping cough and other diseases.

Nurses often brought sick children into the company's purification room. Even gentlemen in carriages sometimes brought in their small sons and daughters for a few whiffs of the efficacious lime gases.

(These latter contentions were true. As a matter of fact, the company's purification room was overrun with sick youngsters, and the company had been about to close it to the public. Until just now, the company had considered the children a nuisance.)

But the Board of Health was adamant, and at last the company was obliged to purify its purifying process.

Under such circumstances as these, it was inevitable that existing gas companies should appear shaky, and that new ones should arise and attempt to knock them off. The first of the gas wars had been between the New York and the Manhattan. Now in 1861 a new war broke out as the Manhattan was itself invaded. The new company called itself the Metropolitan. Somehow it had staggered into existence without backing, without money, without even officers who believed in it—in one month seven of them gave up hope and resigned; in another month twelve. Shares of its stock, bought at $10, were being traded for drinks in corner saloons.

The Manhattan, trying to deliver a knockout blow, sent its trench diggers up Broadway, up Third Avenue, north of Forty-second Street. Mains were swiftly buried and filled with gas. Possession seemed nine-tenths of the law. There would be no territory left for the new company, and it would succumb to the might of the Manhattan.

But the Civil War gave the Metropolitan a breathing spell. It acquired stability, backing, built a plant, laid its own mains. The Manhattan then decided to compromise. The Metropolitan could have all territory between Thirty-fourth and Seventy-ninth streets; in return, all the Manhattan wanted was about sixty per cent of the Metropolitan's stock. This agreement was signed, and everybody breathed a sigh of relief.

There were now four gas companies and the island was neatly divided among them. Everybody made money. The situation was too good to last.

Not all schemes for cheaper, brighter gas were as wild as

the one propounded by the garbage man. In 1872 a new company, the Mutual, lifted a torch into the night above the city, which flamed more brilliantly than any of the others. The Mutual had learned to make gas from naphtha! New York was astonished. Not only was the new gaslight four or five candlepower brighter, it also was much cheaper.

The Mutual Company pushed its advantage with vigor and imagination, bragging publicly that it would lay its twenty-four-inch mains—largest in the world—in the territories of all the older companies.

The Mutual's first customer was a saloon across the street from its plant at Eleventh Street and the East River, hardly a historic beginning. But naphtha gas caught on fast. Before long, meter readers of the Manhattan and Metropolitan began reporting that subscribers were no longer using the old gas. In place of the old meter, there now was a new one on the cellar floor marked: Mutual.

The company began to lay competing mains in all the streets. Within four years it had passed all other companies except the Manhattan and was second in sales. The Manhattan, though still first, was groggy and bleeding; its business had been cut ten per cent.

The raiding had just begun. In 1875 the Municipal Gas Light Company was formed. Its new water gas was as much superior to naphtha gas as naphtha gas had been to coal gas.

The war was on for fair, now. The Knickerbocker Company was formed in 1878 and promptly laid fifty miles of mains, most of it in territory which had belonged exclusively to the Harlem. The next year it laid twenty miles more, some of it thirty inches in diameter, pipes that looked colossal as they went into the ground.

In 1880 peace of a kind came to the warring gas companies, and in 1884 they consolidated. They had to. A new menace had loomed on the horizon, fiercer and more implacable than anything they had yet known.

Thomas Edison had discovered how to make light from electricity.

12. Edison's Magic "Flooid"

CONFRONTED BY EDISON'S incandescent light, the gas industry huddled together in fear and trembling, completely demoralized. Gaslighting—and the gas industry, it seemed—was doomed. The new light was of "stupefying" brilliance, as superior to gas lamps as the gas had been to oil lamps so many years before. Why, the mere fact that all lampposts could be turned on within ten minutes—as against the hour needed by a legion of lamplighters—was an unassailable advantage.

Frantic gas executives spent all of their waking hours, plus many formerly devoted to sleeping, in attempts to find a flaw in the brilliance of electric light. There must be something wrong with it.

First, it was hoped to compete with electricity on a strictly quality basis. Methods were sought to pep up the light which gas burners gave. Reliability was another word with which the gas industry hoped to stay the stampede to electricity. Edison's bulbs burned out, but gas was always available. And new transfer mains were put down which would make it possible to send gas from any part of the understreet network to any other part. This meant that if a main broke or sprung a leak, gas could be piped in from some other direction. Service would not be interrupted.

The transfer system was a stroke of engineering genius; much of it is still in service today and no reconstruction was ever necessary because of faulty planning. In places the company is still adding to the original grid.

But the electric assault was barely dented. Gas employees knew this, even though their superiors refused the surrender which was believed imminent. The workers sat in little groups at lunchtime to talk the electric light back and forth, believing that their jobs at the gas plant were as good as lost. The Brush Electric Illuminating Company and the United States Illuminating Company had already received contracts to light the city's streets and parks. Outdoor gaslights had been snuffed out. Indoor lighting was next. (Only the Harlem Company, out of range of the electric generators, was still lighting public streets.)

Meanwhile, the board at the Stock Exchange seemed manipulated by madmen. Edison stock soon had zoomed to $500 a share, then $3,000, then $5,000, then $8,000. Sometimes it advanced $100 an hour, even though Edison had yet to lay his few miles of wire, or begin supplying his fifty-nine private customers.

The gas people were in despair. Next week or next month might see them all bankrupt; no one had yet thought of selling gas for cooking or heating.

Meanwhile the electric people were so full of high spirits that they went around relating the newest "electric" anecdote.

There was, for instance, the tale of the two Irishmen who were laying telegraph conduits under the city streets. One of them, Rafferty, had been in the country only a year, so his pal, Mulcahy, was explaining to him why the wires were insulated, not "naked in the trenches."

"Becuz the flooid wud lake out an' spill the messages," explained Mulcahy, digging deep into his vast store of electrical knowledge.

Rafferty kept asking questions, and Mulcahy, who had reached America only a year or two before Rafferty, kept firing back answers. Rafferty soon learned that the "flooid's" other name was 'lectricity. that it had been originally discovered by the Western Union Company in cats, had been boiled out in great quantities, and was now kept in an immense number of jars under the Western Union Building on Broadway. The jars were sent around to other cities like Philadelphia, Baltimore and Chicago, as required.

Emergency service at the turn of the century.

Overhead wires, wrecked by the Blizzard of '88, were soon to go underground.

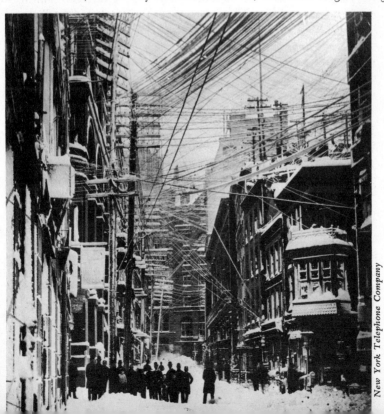

A pair of linemen, overhearing this scientific conversation, informed Rafferty that they would fill a bottle with the magic "flooid" for him, anytime he wanted.

In a moment, Rafferty was back with an empty beer bottle.

"You fill it with this," said one of the linemen, lifting a wire with gloved fingers and tossing it over. "Catch."

The unsuspecting Rafferty caught the bare wire in his bare hands. The shock jarred him to the roots of his molars. After he had stopped screaming he made for the two linemen with murder in his eye.

The two linemen were laughing uproariously as they dodged Rafferty's rushes, their ears ringing with Rafferty's wounded roar.

A policeman ran up and threatened to throw everybody in the cooler for disturbing the peace.

"Give us a break," whined the linemen.

"I think," said the cop in a brogue as rich as Rafferty's, "that the two of you owe this man an apology and a drink."

In this way the dispute was settled out of court. In fact, it was settled at the corner saloon. First the two linemen bought a round, then Rafferty, then Mulcahy, then the cop. It was about five hours later that the men parted, so the story goes, full of scientific good feeling and Harlem rye.

No one understood very much about electricity. The new light sockets were lashed to gas fixtures and the wires nailed to the walls or ceiling. Where two or more lights hung from crystal chandeliers sparks would fly back and forth during thunderstorms, terrifying the uninitiated consumers.

People actually did believe that electricity was a fluid which flowed through the wires under the street into their homes.

"There is much talk of the 'electric fluid,'" wrote the Washington Post. "It is not a fluid or any form of water." The Post, unable to explain just what electricity was if not a fluid, concluded weakly that the current was in any case "lively; it must be admitted to be lively."

Edison himself was fond of telling the story of the ragman's horse. One afternoon a policeman rushed into the Pearl St. plant and told Edison to send an electrician uptown quick, there was some trouble.

Edison ran to the spot, where he found a crowd of men and boys. "There was a leak in one of our junction boxes," he later reported, and "on account of the cellars extending under the street, the moist top soil had become charged."

As Edison reached the place, the dilapidated old horse and cart of a ragman plodded around the corner. The charged earth had been discovered after some pedestrians had been jolted by shocks and now a boy decided to send an old man and his horse across it as a prank.

"This way, old man," he called. "Watch out for the other side. Come this way."

The crowd leaned forward in anticipation. Even Edison made no move of warning.

The old man, alarmed, switched his horse across the withers and steered it for what was, he thought, safe ground.

The instant the horse struck the electrified soil, it reared and stood straight in the air. Down it came, then reared again. The crowd roared with delight as the horse bolted, the old ragman screaming and shouting. In a moment it was out of sight.

The next morning a stranger turned up at the Pearl Street plant and asked to see Edison. He identified himself as a horse dealer.

"I seen what happened to that ragman's horse yesterday," he explained. "I want you to lay an apparatus like that at my stable. We can both make a fortune out of it—buying old nags and selling them for thoroughbreds. Why that ragman's horse was jumping around like a two year old!"

Edison, laughing, declined the offer.

From the beginning there were several electric companies, most of whom strung their wires from rooftop to rooftop, planting great poles to carry the wires in spots where no buildings existed.

Edison believed in running his wires through conduits under the streets. Accordingly, he had begun laying mains in the summer of 1881. Orders were coming in faster than he could fill them, particularly since he had to educate workers first—a night school was opened at 65 Fifth Avenue to bridge the electrical gaps in the knowledge of his men.

During the laying of his tubes, Edison was ordered to the office of the Commissioner of Public Works.

"You are putting down these tubes," the Commissioner said. "You need five inspectors to look after this work. Their salary is five dollars a day. Good morning."

Edison left the office worried and upset, though not about the moral or financial aspects of the case. Few men knew the first thing about electricity; certainly the five inspectors would not. As always, Edison was in a hurry. He was working his crews night and day, and now he expected to be delayed and harassed by officious, ignorant inspectors.

He waited nervously for the inspectors to appear. They did, finally—on Saturday afternoon to collect their pay. Then they went away and were not seen again until the following Saturday afternoon. Edison breathed a sigh of relief. To him, $150 a week in inspectors' fees seemed a cheap price to pay for non-interference. Edison had a fantastic instinct for invention, but none at all for moral indignation. To pay graft bothered him not a bit.

By October 1, 1882, Edison had strung his wires through the street conduits and into the homes of fifty-nine private customers. By December 1, 144 more homes were added to his network. A year later the total of clients was 513. Even the Sixth Avenue El which Dr. Gilbert had built, but which was now run by Cyrus Field, switched to electric lighting in its cars.

"Cyrus," noted the New York *Times* sarcastically, "is kept continually in a mood of jubilant expectancy [over the new lights], excited, oratorical and gurgling.

"The action of the locomotive's machinery is to . . . generate the electric current; when the engine is at work there will be light; when the engine stops there will be no light. When someone suggests that any mishap . . . would plunge the whole train into darkness, Cyrus replies in his lion-hearted, philanthropic way that that would be visiting the darkness upon the just and the unjust alike. This sweet spirited style of philosophy might not inspire the average traveller as much as it tickles Cyrus . . . it wouldn't be a pleasant sensation for every railway passenger to feel that he must keep his hand clapped over his trousers pocket every time a brakeman yells out a station all the way up to the Harlem."

The decade from 1880 to 1890 was one of the busiest periods so far under the streets of New York, and the "drivers" and pedestrians of the day must have cursed the ubiquitous excavations and incessant jams even more heartily than the modern New Yorker does today—for no one really knew just what purpose the uproar in the streets was intended to serve.

Not only was the gas industry, sick with the apparent futility of its position, laying heavy transfer mains; not only was Edison busily ripping up pavement to string his pesky wires; but also those years saw the birth of the New York Steam Company now a subsidiary of Con Edison. It, too, was digging trenches and laying pipe.

Most of this work was done at night. Edison personally supervised his crews, as did C. E. Emery, chief engineer of the embryonic steam company.

During the pre-dawn hours, Maiden Lane was as quiet and empty then as it is today—except for the ringing noise of picks and shovels cutting through the roof of the island.

Sometimes in the night, when all was quiet except for the wind whistling around the high buildings, when even their crews had gone home to bed, Edison and Emery would meet at a street corner, have a smoke together, and talk about the chances of their respective schemes ever catching on. The world would count both of them geniuses later on, but now they were just worried young men trying something which had never been tried before. They were nervous and unsure of themselves.

"I thought he had a harder proposition than I had," Edison recalled many years later, "and he thought that mine was harder than his." (Emery was competing with a second steam company which was also laying pipes at this time.) "But one thing we both agreed on, that this other steam heating engineer hadn't any chance at all, and that his company would surely fail. . . . Emery used mineral wool to surround his pipes, which was of a fibrous nature and was stuffed in boxes to prevent loss of heat and pressure, whereas his competitor was laying his pipes in square boxes filled with lampblack.

"Before Emery had finished all his pipes and was working in the street one night, he heard a terrible rush of steam. It seems his competitor had put on steam pressure to test out his pipes. There was a leak in the pipe; the steam got into the lampblack and blew up, throwing three tons of lampblack all over the place and covering fronts of several stores in Maiden Lane. When the people came down next morning, everything was covered with lampblack—and the company 'busted'!"

About this time the sagging Consolidated Gas Company pulled itself together and discovered that gas was something a person could cook with, too. The company forthwith began to subsidize companies and stores selling stoves, and to seek whatever means it could to draw attention to itself. All was *not* lost. The fear that the gas company's mains would forever lie empty and molding in the ground was baseless.

The *Times* reported one of the key events in the gas company's recovery:

"Fifty well-known cooks met yesterday at Tammany Hall to witness a demonstration of cooking with gas.

"The appearance of the big hall was absolutely unsuggestive of politics. Three ponderous gas stoves, connected by a big black pipe and ornamented with taps of all sizes, stood at one side of the room. Then there was a long table filled with uncooked good things—oysters . . . filet de sole . . . lobsters . . . steaks . . . and a variety of other dainties. . . .

"There was a slight shiver to be noticed about the persons of the assembled multitude when it was announced that everything cooked in Tammany Hall was to be eaten. . . . One of Delmonico's cooks turned distinctly and undeniably pale, and the cook at the Downtown Club grasped the back of a convenient chair."

When the food had been sufficiently admired, "the three chefs de service dexterously opened the stoves and inserted chickens, beef, steaks and other things into the ovens. They then carefully adjusted the jets of gas, and banging the doors, awaited results, while guests looked with as much interest as though the stoves were crematories."

The meal prepared was, the *Times* correspondent reported, quite tasty.

With publicity like this in its favor, the gas industry was soon on its feet again.

By then also, electricity was in trouble. Little did anyone suspect that the city's streets, currently ablaze with electric arc lights, would soon be lighted only by gas again.

13. The Day They Chopped the Poles Down

AMONG THE ELECTRIC-LIGHT pioneers, only Edison had the foresight and good taste to string his wires through conduits under the streets of the city. To the others the use of telegraph poles seemed simpler and a good deal cheaper.

They planted their poles in the sidewalks, one company after another: the Western Union Telegraph Company, the Gold and Stock Ticker Company, the United States, Brush and East River Electric Lighting companies, the telephone company; as well as companies representing the fire department (warning systems), the police department (traffic signals), and various private and public burglar-alarm firms.

Companies rarely shared poles; each erected its own. Poles were of varying heights so as not to interfere with each other's lines. Many were fifty feet high, the height of a five-story building. Others towered sixty feet above the street—or even ninety. The poles supporting the arc lights which illuminated Union Square were said to be 150 feet high, and the great arc lamps themselves were tremendous iron structures weighing over two hundred pounds.

Some of the poles carried seven or ten or a dozen crosstrees, outstretched arms as closely spaced as railroad ties, each loaded with twenty or more wires. Single poles were freighted with a hundred wires, or two hundred. Through this mass of wires other poles might poke, carrying a second bank of wires along the same street in the same direction, the second bank as dense as the first. In places a man could stand on the sidewalk peering up toward a sky he couldn't see because the hundreds of wires were laced together as impenetrably as the canopy of leaves of a tree in summer.

Wires ran in all directions and were a positive menace in times of storm or fire. Heavy snow brought down hundreds of them. When fire broke out, the department might race to the scene of the blaze, but it did not throw up its ladders in haste. It raised them gingerly up through the delicate, innocent-looking wires, while the flames roared and an occasional citizen got roasted alive. More than one fireman was electrocuted too, ducking away from a falling timber into a lethal wire. Often pieces of the burning building (and much of the city was of wood and combustible in the 1880's) would break a wire which then would fall to the street to burn or kill.

The blizzard of '88 was the last straw. A law had been passed as early as 1884, ordering all companies to string their wires through subways. (The term "subways" appears to have been invented to describe the new understreet conduits. Subways as we know them today were still called "underground railways." And, of course, none were as yet in existence, except for the sealed and molding Beach tube.)

Following the 1884 decree, a "subway" company came into being which began to lay some conduits and to string some wire through them. But the major companies were having none of it. They blandly ignored the new law, and continued to hang their wires to the overburdened poles. Conduits seemed an unnecessary expense. The companies were absolutely essential to the city, were they not? The city would not, and could not, force them underground.

While citizens howled that the wires "disfigured their fair city," the various companies grew fat and complacent. Municipal authority waited patiently.

Then came the blizzard of '88. Snow fell heavily on the lacework of wires and stuck there. It turned to ice; then, as the wind whipped fiercely, the whole system seemed to come crashing down at once. For days the wires lay in the streets. In some places where the snow was hard packed, the deadly wires writhed about like snakes. The city was terrified. Thousands of people were afraid to venture abroad at all, until the companies at last announced that all was clear.

The wrath of the city, now aroused beyond all reckoning, could no longer be smothered by the companies, however rich or essential they might be. The election swept to office Mayor Hugh J. Grant, who swore to do something about the wires.

Almost his first official act was to announce angrily that if the wires were not removed at once, he would cut them down himself.

"He's kidding—" said the companies, "isn't he?"

Grant was not kidding. Legal machinery was started at once to permit the Mayor, as President of the Board of Electrical Control, to snip off the wires and chop down the poles.

In March, 1889, Jay Gould, head of Western Union, secured an injunction against "this impetuous mayor."

Two weeks later the court again handed down an order, empowering Grant to start chopping. With Gould's process server presumably waiting in the corridor to serve the Mayor with another injunction, Mayor Grant ingeniously disappeared for a few hours, so that the process server could not find him. By the time the Mayor turned up again, axmen were at work in the streets. New York was about to be purged of its hated poles and wires.

Orders were sent to all companies to cut off current on the wires at once.

At Fourteenth Street and Broadway two gangs of ten men each gathered, surrounded by a "large and festive" crowd. A man came running up, waving the court order above his head. The crowd began to cheer.

"At last," breathed Mr. Richardson whom the city had appointed superintendent of the gangs.

Richardson, his men and his wagonload of axes and nippers had been waiting on that corner for nearly two weeks, anxious to start chopping. Like most working men, Richardson had no understanding of, nor use for legal obstructions—they left him angry, disgusted with what he judged were spineless superiors. Now, worked up to a fever, he set out on a crusade to cut and destroy the steel and wire tentacles of the octopus which was strangling the city.

At his signal, men strapped on their climbing gear. In a moment one of them was atop the nearest pole. His leg looped over the crosstree, the man began snipping. The first wire fell to the street.

Before long the pole was cleared of all wires running north, the two gangs had split up, and were proceeding up both sides of Broadway, delightedly snipping wires and felling the mighty poles. Down came Brush Electric Light wires, Gold and Stock ticker wires, East River Electric Light wires. Only the police and fire alarm poles were allowed to stand; the burial of these wires had already been scheduled by the city for a day or two later.

By now Union Square and streets leading into it were black with people, many of whom were good-naturedly guying the workers. The police were hurriedly summoned to hold back this crowd; there was danger that a hot wire or rotted pole might fall upon it.

The initial wires cut were ticker wires. They fell peacefully to the street. But when the gang's nippers cut into the first Brush wire a shower of sparks shot out—these wires were far from dead. A scream rose from the spectators as the lethal wire fell to earth, just missing them. It lashed about on the pavement, hissing blue sparks. Quickly a man clambered up the next pole and cut its other end, depriving the hanging wire of its terrible power.

The crowd had recoiled, as if from a snake. People had fallen and been trampled. Befuddled, an old couple, holding hands like teen-agers, had in their fright darted into the street straight toward the wire. A cop grabbed them just in time.

"The death current," cried persons in the crowd. "The company has turned on the death current!"

Death current or not, the rubber-gloved climbers went on clipping Brush Company wires with their rubber-handled shears. However, they changed tactics. Now men mounted adjacent poles simultaneously. They would pick out a wire and clip it from both ends at once. That way it was dead when it hit the street and could be safely rolled up and loaded onto the wagon.

When each pole was naked, except for stubs of wire on the crosstrees, guy ropes were attached. Then men attacked the base of the pole with axes. When the pole was ready to fall, traffic and sight-seers were backed up and the pole was allowed to sag slowly to the street.

Toward noon, Foreman Sears of the Brush Company appeared with a wagon, having been ordered to coil and load each section of Brush wire as it fell.

Richardson, still filled with righteous indignation, grabbed Sears by the shoulder and spun him around.

"What do you think you're doing?"

"I've come for our wire."

"I guess you haven't heard. This wire is confiscated by the city."

"What for?" demanded Sears.

"To pay the cost of taking it down."

Sears got so angry he began to rant and rave in a manner which the dense crowd found highly entertaining. Just then the last of the wires was cut from a certain pole which, rotted at the base, suddenly toppled. As it fell a horse-drawn omnibus was plodding up the street. A scream rose from the crowd as the pole fell toward the horsecar.

With a great crash, the pole struck precisely between the hands of the driver and the tails of the horses. The horses reared and whinnied, but could not run away—the tremendous weight of the pole had pinned their harness to the street. The passengers were helped to alight; two women, when they saw how narrowly they had missed being crushed, fainted on the spot.

Such excitement was too much for Sears, who lost his head completely. Springing to the platform of the car, he thrust a finger toward the nearest cop and screamed:

"Arrest them. Arrest them!"

"Arrest who?" asked the cop.

"Arrest everybody!"

The crowd, released from the sudden tension, found the frantic Sears completely funny. It howled with laughter.

Only the crusading Richardson was not amused.

"You have thirty seconds to make yourself scarce around here," he told Sears. "If you don't I'll have you arrested."

The crowd roared again.

Sears slunk away after that, and was not seen again until evening when, according to one observer, "he seemed in an easier frame of mind."

The wires were thick and the work slow. Following a noon recess, work continued until five, then resumed the next morning at six. Only three blocks were cleared the first day and it was decided to add extra gangs to speed things up.

The reaction of the companies was curious. The angry Brush Company, mirroring the temperament of Sears, threatened to quit lighting the city if any more of its wires were torn down. When the city, in effect, laughed in the company's face, the faithful Sears was sent back to Broadway to harass Richardson again.

Sears had a crew with him this time and as soon as a Brush wire fell he sent his men scurrying after it, yelling, "Load 'er in the truck, boys."

"Are you back again?" screamed Richardson.

"It's our wire," cried the tenacious Sears.

"That wire is confiscated. Now get out of here or I'll send every single one of you to jail."

This time Sears went meekly away and did not come back.

Jay Gould's Western Union, on the other hand, welcomed the axmen. His earlier injunctions had served their purpose —his men had had time to string telegraph wires in the conduits. Now the wire aloft was dead, the poles a nuisance, and the city was actually saving Gould money by chopping them down for him.

However, Gould resented losing the Gold and Stock ticker wires, a company which he also controlled. When the city, a few days later, was obliged to attach some fire alarm wires to Gould's El structure, Gould got his merry revenge. He sent out men with nippers and cut them down.

The Metropolitan Company tried to transfer its wires from doomed poles to rooftops where, theoretically, they would be safe from Richardson's men. Richardson sent a cop to arrest one of the linemen on the charge of putting up wires without a permit, and that ended that.

Shrewdest and most successful of the companies was the United States Illuminating. Its crews started a block ahead of Richardson's choppers—and stayed a block ahead all week, hurriedly rolling up wire and carting it away, in some cases only a few minutes before the confiscatory Richardson got there. Richardson was left to truncate block after block of barren poles—the most difficult, most perilous and least pleasing aspect of the job.

New York at night was again lighted by gas, dimly, dimally lighted, according to all accounts. "Broadway," wrote one observer, "seemed plunged into darkness." As the Broadway cars mounted the island they passed from the arc-lighted districts below Fourteenth Street to the now-gaslighted district above. "It was like leaving the light of day and entering a tunnel." "Madison Square," wrote one journalist mournfully, "was like a country churchyard, and the city was sepulchral. Saloons were more popular than ever."

From the beginning the work proceeded carefully and the most serious accident occurred when a stylishly dressed young woman stubbed her toe on the stump of a pole which had not been evened off. Because she was so young, so pretty and suffered so keenly all of New York was upset about her, supposing, since she had had to be taken home in a cab, that she had broken her dainty foot.

Then an accident occurred which removed the work altogether from the joke category.

Two linemen, Mike Early and Hugh Reilly, were sent up to the roof of a building to belay guy ropes steadying a ninety-foot pole which had been stripped of its wires. In the street—this was at Sixth Avenue and Thirty-fifth—an estimated thousand persons watched in awe as axmen attacked the great trunk of the pole.

But Early and Reilly, unable to find a sturdy anchor for their guy ropes on the roof, had descended to a third-floor bedroom. There was nothing to lash the rope to there, either, so they stuck a crowbar against the window frame and wrapped their rope around that.

Below, axes had cut through the trunk, and the huge pole tottered. In the bedroom window, the rope around the crowbar grew taut, as Reilly and Early hung on, putting their backs and shoulders into it, leaning against the rope, their bodies quivering from the strain. Then, with a shudder and a crash, the whole side of the building ripped out, yanking Reilly and Early, entangled in the rope, behind it.

The men struck the sidewalk with terrific impact. Early landed on his face and was killed instantly. Reilly's body was horribly broken, but he was still alive and was carried tenderly into the nearest saloon while a horse-drawn ambulance was summoned.

In the street the crowd was screaming its horror. Some persons had become ill, there were tears and wailing. Someone turned Early over. His face was mashed beyond belief, unrecognizable. A burly lineman draped his handkerchief over Early's face to hide it.

That tragedy lingered in the minds and hearts of the city. Day by day work continued, but wire and poles came down soberly now. The crowds diminished. People realized they had not been watching horseplay, but serious men faced with a serious task. The wires had to come down and go underground, even if men died. The growth, the future of the city demanded it. Progress has never been bought cheaply.

14. Rats Under the Piecrust

ANY NEW YORKER will tell you that the city's two swankiest avenues are Park and Fifth; but few are aware that beneath the chic veneer, both are plagued by rats. Under Fifth Avenue, rats drive the Con Edison people crazy, for they find the insulation around Con Edison's high voltage cables much to their taste. This does not do the cables any good, nor the rats either. The rats don't know when to stop. They find the insulation so appetizing that they eat right down to the bare cable—and for days after that the tunnel reeks of fried rats. Sometimes the odor is so strong you can smell it in the street.

Con Edison has tried everything, short of replacing every foot of cable with something less delicious. But nothing, as yet, works. Exterminating companies have trimmed the rat population somewhat, however.

The rat palate apparently is not pleased by telephone insulation, and those lines never are nibbled at all. Real gourmets, those rats.

At Park Avenue the situation is even worse. Park Avenue is a piecrust, beneath which trains from upstate and New England enter Grand Central Station on two levels, fanning out onto forty-eight tracks. The street surface of Park Avenue is only a few inches thick. The grass island down the center of it is too shallow to support the roots of shade trees. The buildings which flank it, even the mighty, forty-seven-story Waldorf-Astoria Hotel, have no basements—the Waldorf's wine celler is on the fifth floor—or heating plants of their own. They were

148

built without chimneys and they buy their heat from the New York Steam Company. The steam company also takes the chill off most of the financial district, but there it got the contract because it could do the job cheaper and more neatly than the individual buildings could. Along Park Avenue there could be no dickering.

The foundations along Park Avenue end a half inch below sidewalk level. Below that they are balanced atop stilts like any bamboo house in the jungle, except that the stilts in this case are great concrete pillars sunk to bedrock, six hundred trains a day snaking in and out among them, bound for or leaving Grand Central Station.

The area under the piecrust is huge, 79 acres. It includes a five-track turn-around loop passing under both the Biltmore and Commodore hotels. It includes a parking lot for private railroad cars under the Waldorf—in the old days, presidents and other dignitaries arrived in New York by train, not air, and they invariably arrived under the Waldorf, not at Grand Central. This simplified security. In teeming Grand Central, the Great Man would have needed an army to protect him. Under the Waldorf he could alight in privacy, step into the elevator and be lifted directly to his suite. When departing, the same procedure would be followed, saving the people of New York from countless farewell addresses which otherwise would surely have poured down upon them.

Under Park Avenue there even were sidings which were built as parking spaces for the handcars on which railroad executives used to pump themselves to work from their uptown mansions. This practice has been discontinued now (so have mansions), but in the old days it was very much the rage. Nattily dressed executives would kiss their wives good day, drop down a trap-door to their handcars, place their briefcases in a rack and, in a matter of minutes, glide into Grand Central where liveried lackeys waited to stable their steeds. At the end, some of the handcars even had been electrified. Then increased traffic halted their use for all time.

But most of all, the great dark prairie under the piecrust was a paradise for rats. They frolicked and gamboled about the tracks, utterly fearless. They frightened and sometimes bit trackwalkers. They gnawed through insulation and caused fires. They sharpened their teeth on lead pipes. There were hordes of them, big, brown, snub-nosed Norway rats. They got into the shops and hotels overhead. Once one got into a ladies' room at a theater; when finally cornered by an angry man wielding a wrench, the rat attacked.

By 1933 the New York Central could stand it no longer. The tracks south of Sixtieth Street belonged not to the railroads but to the rats, a jungle in which the law of claw and fang prevailed. A high-priced exterminating firm was called in and given the exclusive job of ridding the tracks of rats. Within a month, bounty hunters had things under control—five men had averaged something over two hundred dead rats a day. Those that remained did not disport themselves as publicly as before.

Nevertheless, the war was not over, nor is it even today. Rats carry two known diseases, typhus and bubonic plague, and they are sometimes rabid. The New York Central is still obliged to file regular rat reports with the city health department, and there are occasional surprise inspections of the tunnel by health officials searching for a "special." A "special" in the trade is a live rat. As the official makes his rounds he will find plenty of dead rats along runways where poisonous goodies have been left about by the exterminating firm; he may even find a specimen struggling to extract itself from a board coated with deep glue, a curious kind of trap which the firm sometimes favors.

But if the official finds a true "special" it is considered a disaster and heads roll—not only rats' heads, either.

There are more rats in the tunnel in winter than in summer, when, presumably, they play about in the streets. To kill them a special poison compound is sprinkled over or inserted into various baits. Zwieback is good. Also cornmeal, oatmeal, fats and fruit. But rats are choosy. They will only eat fruit which is ripe, and they are known to have a special weakness for canteloupe and honeydew melon.

In the days when hamburger cost fifteen cents a pound, meat was sometimes used but, as the saying goes, them days is gone forever. There are tricks. Rat runaways can be found by looking for a greasy line along the base of a wall—rats' coats are oily and traces of their favorite routes are easy to find. Baits must never be handled; rats know the human scent and avoid it. Baits can often be made maddeningly attractive. Touch a match to a piece of bacon, for instance, and rats come running. It's an aroma they seem to find irresistible.

Nowadays, the line of "no rat land" in the tunnel has been marked off at Fifty-ninth Street. It is presumed that the rats enter through the north end of the tunnel at Ninety-sixth, and that by the time they reach Fifty-ninth they are hungry and will search out the baits.

About sixty pounds of bait a day are still laid out under the piecrust, but they victimize only about one hundred rats a month—the rat population there is well under control. The plywood shingles, thick with special black glue, sometimes are used, but the firm's men have found that stuck rats often will bite off their own paws rather than remain glued to the shingle until the men come round.

The men who plant the baits (and later dispose of the corpses) are mostly quiet, non-introspective types, who are contemptuous of what they term "tall rat stories."

They will tell you that their variety of rat is sixteen inches long, half of it being tail, then add: "I never met a guy yet seen a small rat. The rats they seen are all big as cats—as dogs, even."

One of the questions rat men are most often asked is: "Have you read 'The Pied Piper of Hamelin'?"

This is sure to provoke a disgusted response, such as: "I got better weapons than a blankety-blank flute."

Are the city's rat killers essential?

It might seem so: Rats litter when they are eight weeks old, have three to twelve litters a year, and there are from six to twenty-two young per litter. It has been figured that two rats, left alone, would produce five million descendants in a single year!

By even conservative estimates there are, despite the rat killers, eight million rats living beneath the streets of New York today.

The first trains to run into Grand Central were the steam

locomotives of the New York and Harlem Railroad. This was back in the mid-nineteenth century, the tracks were not roofed over and there were stops at many points along the way.

Bear this in mind as you read the tale of the elderly woman who in 1955 kept phoning the police to report seeing men with sacks on their backs disappearing down manholes near Ninetieth Street at Park Avenue. No, she had never seen any of the men come out. Do you suppose they were murderers disposing of their victims' bodies down there?

To the police, who receive hundreds of calls a day just like this one, the woman sounded balmy. But she was persistent. They had to admit she was persistent.

Finally, to humor her, they gave instructions to be called instantly the next time the men with sacks showed up. Sure enough, a few days later the woman phoned back. Five of the men had just dropped down a manhole. She had been sitting in the window of her apartment and had seen them.

The patrol car arrived in a few minutes. The woman was waiting outside and she directed the policemen to the manhole in question. They raised it gingerly, not knowing what to expect. They peered in, but saw nothing, listened intently, but heard nothing.

Was the woman completely cracked? Had she imagined everything?

The cops climbed down into the manhole. Ahead they spied a glimmer of light. They walked toward it.

They were experienced men, but the sight which next met their eyes astonished them.

They had stumbled upon a long-abandoned station platform of the old New York and Harlem Railroad—in which a gang of hoboes had set up housekeeping.

The station, once on the main line, now was partially walled up, forming a sort of alcove hidden from both track walkers and the trains of the New York Central.

Inside the alcove the bums lived comfortably, even cozily. The old carbon lamps on the walls had been lighted, and gave a faint, almost bluish glow to the place. Clothesline had been stretched across here and there; on some of them, the cops noted, laundry was drying. The pallets and mattresses on which the bums slept, were ranked against the walls as in a barracks. The sacks which the old woman had reported, lay limply about. The cops could see what they had contained: old clothes, newspapers, food, bits of garbage scavenged from neighborhood cans which might still be found serviceable.

The intruders did not remain flabbergasted long. Nor did they pause to admire overmuch the fantastic ingenuity of the bums who had discovered and outfitted the abandoned station. Being cops, they merely drew their night sticks and waded in flailing. Down came the clotheslines and laundry. Up went the straw pallets, kicked to pieces by heavy shoes. The fire around which the startled bums had been cooking their lunch was doused by a bucket of water.

The night sticks also cracked against a few skulls. The bums made no fight. In a few moments all of them were gone, having escaped down other passages or up other manholes.

For a while after that the police checked back to make sure the bums had not returned.

"Imagine the noive of them bums," said one cop. "Under Park Avenue of all places. Couldn't they have picked some dumpy street? What would them swells along Park Avenue have said if they'd known they was living right on top of a hobo jungle?"

15. The Great Sewer Scandal

THE BOROUGH OF QUEENS of the City of New York sits atop that flat, soggy portion of Long Island just east of midtown Manhattan. It is the largest of the five boroughs in area, and probably the poorest in real estate value. Three bodies of water bathe its shores, the Atlantic Ocean, Long Island Sound and the East River, and it seems to lie in the path of every squall and tempest which whips up the east coast from the Caribbean. Queens is so low that the rains which pour upon it do not drain well—sometimes they do not drain at all. From earliest times it has needed good sewers more than any of the other boroughs, but it has only recently begun to get them.

The sewer history of Queens has always been turgid. Recently a seventy-five-year-old man, walking home at night in a storm, tripped and drowned on a street corner in the Queens Village section of the borough. There were four to five feet of water in the streets when the police found him—and no storm sewers under them, despite a campaign for flood relief by residents which had been going on thirty years. A woman said she had heard a cry for help while examining her water-filled basement.

"I looked out the window, but it was so dark I couldn't see anything. I thought I was imagining things."

And so the old man lay all night in his watery shroud.

It was a grim experience for Queens, but there have been others equally shocking. There is one busy intersection lined with vacant, staring store fronts. Hundreds of merchants have

154

tried to do business there. Some, unsuspecting, were overjoyed as they moved in; crowds of people passed their doors every hour; the rent was low. Perhaps suspicion began when they found out how high insurance rates were.

The first serious rainstorm usually destroyed the hope these merchants may have had for success. It also destroyed any stock they may have stored in their basements. For days the water would rush down the streets and sidewalks well above curb level. Inside, the despairing merchants could spend their time trying to wring out and salvage soggy goods. There would be no business, no traffic outside their doors until the flood in the streets subsided.

At present, what are believed to be the world's largest sewers have been and are being buried under the streets of Queens. It is hoped that these corridor sewers, some twenty-five feet wide, will remedy the situation somewhat.

The corridor sewers are expensive, but their price is low compared to the sewers which were built in Queens prior to 1927. These were the most expensive sewers the world had ever known. They were so expensive that one man made a profit of more than a million dollars a year in 1925, 1926 and 1927—on pipe alone. A $6,000-a-year city engineer banked ten times his salary. The Borough President bought for cash real estate worth $146,000.

Meanwhile, homeowners in Queens were ordered to pay staggering assessments—some had to mortgage their homes, cars and businesses to do so. In other families, hard up even before the sewer assessments, the parents went without overcoats all winter, and the children went without toys at Christmas.

Investigations had been smothered every year since 1921. But in 1927 outrage became overwhelming and an ugly scandal erupted. Testimony was given, grand juries sat and deliberated, and indictments were handed down. For nearly five years the Great Sewer Scandal smoldered on page one. The chief figure died under suspicious circumstances. Another man was led to a cemetery in Maspeth, Long Island, and quietly murdered. Seven different offices were broken into and records stolen. Key witnesses disappeared. Some men perjured themselves, others collapsed on the witness stand. Bribes were offered, reportedly as high as $200,000. Some bribes, unreported, evidently were accepted, for in the end nearly everybody got off. Those who didn't were sentenced to the equivalent of a slap on the wrist and were photographed sailing to Europe—first class, of course. The people of Queens went on paying for their sewers.

The scandal broke prosaically enough. A Republican charged that Democratic borough hall was paying four times as much for sewers as the other boroughs—the plot was to assess tax-payers more than $16,000,000 for forty miles of new sewers, he claimed.

"Tammany has permitted the gouging of the people of Queens to go on and on. . . ."

The next day the Board of Assessors called in a borough engineer, whose answers ranged from "Don't know," to "Look it up yourself," to "Never heard of it."

Plainly the board was on to something. Borough President Maurice E. Connolly, for sixteen years the "undisputed ruler of all things political in Queens," explained calmly that the borough was growing fast, it was mostly flat land which did not drain well, so of course sewers were expensive.

Connolly added that the 1921 investigation committee had demonstrated that charges of graft in his administration were mere empty rumors. The Republican's speech, said Connolly, was just another political diatribe. Forget it. Everything was going along fine.

But there was something ugly just under the surface (buried about as far down as a sewer pipe) and everybody knew it. Rumor or not, it was said that Senator Meyer's committee had been bought off in 1921 for a bribe of $100,000. Citizens were only too ready to believe stories like this. The borough had long had an unsavory reputation. Since Queens' incorporation into the city in 1891, one borough president had been sent to Sing Sing for selling a judgeship for $10,000, another was re-moved by the Governor for incompetence and a third, Joseph Bermel, having been elected as a reform candidate ("fearless, able, firm and upright") in 1905 and having sold the city eighty-seven acres of swamp as a park for several hundred thousand dollars in 1907 ("I will make Queens blossom like a rose") resigned suddenly a few nights later and sailed for Europe the next morning—"to take the baths at Carlsbad because of my health."

Going a bit further back, the last Mayor of Long Island City, "Battle Axe" Patrick Gleason, mysteriously toppled overboard when crossing the East River by ferryboat one dark night. Nobody ever found Gleason's wealth, which was so carefully stashed away that its whereabouts was kept in code in Gleason's notebook. Only one other man knew the code, and he died a few days after Gleason, without having had time to get to the buried money.

Now in 1927, Borough President Connolly himself was far from above suspicion. At the time of the removal of his predecessor in 1911, Connolly was thirty years old and a police magistrate, the youngest on the bench. The Board of Aldermen had voted him in at the price, it was whispered, of $10,000 a vote. Connolly, as he leapt into the seat of power in Queens, had demanded a full-scale investigation be mounted which would prove his virtue. This investigation turned up nothing at all, exactly like those which followed it with distressing regularity in Queens during the next sixteen years.

But in 1927 the people could no longer be quieted. The *Evening World* began printing their plaintive stories.

Elizabeth Dunbar was a widow who owned a small house at 104 Platonic Place, Flushing. She was assessed $467.09, including $247.50 for the Myrtle Avenue sewer, $183.89 for the 150th Place sewer, and $20.88 for Bowne Park—plus seven per cent interest for however long it took her to raise the money. Wrote the *World:* "A For Rent sign now graces the lawn of her home." She told a *World* reporter that she didn't mind so much paying for the sewers, at least they were there to benefit someone, someday. But Bowne Park didn't exist. (This was the name given to an area of marsh ground near the Sound which, at the time, contained neither paths nor trees and whose "lake" was more a collection of stagnant rainwater than anything else.)

John Berger, a small contractor who owned two acres of vacant land on Valeigh Road, a thousand feet from the Union

Turnpike sewer, was assessed $468 for the Myrtle Avenue sewer
which was three miles away, his land being connected to neither
sewer. Were he ever to build on Valeigh Road he would have
to pay another assessment for the Union Turnpike sewer. He
also was assessed $700 for his home at 31 Locust Place.

Jacob Gescheidt bought a home at 176 Bayside Avenue in
July, 1926, having been told nothing at all of a pending sewer
assessment, which in his case amounted to $1,645.

V. H. Schiffer received the deed to his new home at 149
Murray Street on November 23 from its smiling builder, William Watson. On December 9, Mr. Schiffer was assessed
$215.78 for the Myrtle Avenue sewer.

Mrs. Mary M. Brennan, a widow who owned almost nothing
except her home at 21 Locust Street, spent $686 in lawyer's fees
trying to have her assessment of over $5,000 reduced. She was
obliged to mortgage her home.

Carmine Scocca, a laborer and the father of eight children,
owned a home at 143 Farrington Street in the shadow of the
towering gas tanks of the New York and Queens Gas Company where he worked at an average wage of $32 a week. Scoc-
ca's assessment was over $700, more money than he could
earn in five months. Scocca, desperate, appealed to the real
estate firm which had sold him this poor house, telling him
nothing about the pending sewer assessment. He simply
couldn't pay. He was turned away.

It must be pointed out that all of these homes were in un-
improved neighborhoods, and were worth in 1927 about $5,000
each. The average income of Queens families that year was
$1,275. These people not only were staggered by the amounts
they must pay, but they were absolutely defenseless against
the army of lawyers which now moved into Queens, buying
up tax liens on homes, and forcing families out into the street.

There was one other significant assessment, $550 on the home
and fifty-foot lot of Republican Alderman-elect George U.
Harvey. Harvey, receiving the bill, strode out into the street
and looked around him. Said Harvey later: "The man across
the road must pay as much for the same piece of sewer, and
people behind us for a mile back must pay for that same fifty-
foot stretch of sewer. At the rate charged against me, that one

stretch of fifty feet would alone yield a very lucrative amount of graft."

Now everything seemed to happen at once, events slowly closing in on Borough President Connolly, his luxurious home, his expensive clothes, his chauffeur-driven cars, his extensive real estate holdings.

A triumvirate of contractors announced dramatically that they were prepared to build sewers in Queens for a third of what the borough had been paying.

A group of Queens taxpayers hired Henry H. Klein, a small, sharp-faced, belligerent lawyer to represent them at the hearings, which continued before the Board of Assessors.

And Alderman-elect Harvey listened to the noises long enough to draw up formal charges against Connolly and others, which he laid before Governor Alfred E. Smith.

At Borough Hall, Connolly took a worried look about. He could expect no help from Tammany Hall, which had long resented the existence of his own private political machine in Queens. Also, Connolly had been unwise enough to campaign actively against both Governor Smith and Mayor James Walker at the last elections, and had succeeded in carrying Queens for Walker's opponent. Now Tammany gloated over Connolly's discomfort.

For the moment, Lawyer Klein held the spotlight, his scalpel poised over the diseased flesh of Queens. Klein's first target was James Rice, bumbling, sixty-seven year old, $7,250 a year, chief engineer who had drawn up the specifications for the Queens sewer network. Rice was easy pickings for the aggressive Klein, who succeeded in proving that this "chief engineer" knew nothing whatever about sewers and was in fact ". . . utterly unfit and incompetent. . . . He has been carried along for twelve years as a dummy and rubber stamp!"

Rice wilted and dwindled under the attack. He claimed to have been a British Army captain in India "early in the nineties," a graduate of the Royal Military School at Norwich and the Royal Engineers School at Chatham, and the director of the construction of the Sind-Bishim railway tunnel.

But Klein befuddled him into admitting that the only sewers he had ever built were "such sewers as connected to the barracks"; that the Sind-Bishim tunnel had been "designed by the officers"; that he had been looking for "anything I could get in an engineering way," when he had fallen in with Connolly in 1915; and that his last previous job had been as an insurance investigator in Hartford, Connecticut

Is this the man, asked Klein aggrievedly, responsible for $16,000,000-contracts?

Rice, after this testimony, was done for and so, though it would take some time, were Connolly and the others. Klein, deciding to nail the coffin shut, dispatched a cable to the British War Office in London. The return cable was fast and blunt. There was no record of a person named James Rice in the British Army in India, neither as a captain nor any other rank.

(Later Rice was proved such an easygoing blunderer that he could only have been the dupe of the sewer ring, not an accomplice. He escaped trial, but was forced to retire.)

The testimony of Rice brought the name of John M. Phillips, the "Pipe King" of Queens, into the investigation for the first time. According to specifications written by Rice, only Lock-Joint sewer pipe was acceptable in Queens and, oddly enough, this kind of pipe could be bought only from Phillips.

"In other words," charged Klein, "contractors can do the work only if they can get the pipe from Phillips. They must pay him whatever he asks for it—then they pass this little saving on to the people of Queens!"

Phillips was even richer than Connolly. He owned a $150,000 home at Freeport, a stable of race horses and five Pierce-Arrow cars. Oriental décor was maintained throughout his home, the paint being Chinese lacquer and the servants Japanese, while deep-toned Chinese gongs summoned the Pipe King and his family to their meals.

Phillips also owned a gold dinner service so heavy that it took six men to carry it, which was said to have cost $200,000. This was presented to him at Christmas, 1926, by contractors of the borough, in gratitude for being permitted to buy his pipe, although it happened that the fund fell a bit short and Phillips was obliged to kick in the last $3,000 for the dinner service himself. The Pipe King indeed lived royally, even to gratifying every whim of the Crown Prince, his son Francis, eighteen, on whom he lavished polo ponies, speedboats and other knickknacks.

Around Freeport, Phillips was wildly admired. He was an Elk, a Spanish War Veteran, attended Sunday Mass at the Church of the Redeemer, contributed to police department funds, outfitted the baseball teams and tipped cab drivers $20 when they took him home from the station at night. His opulently built, bleached-blond third wife contributed six hundred pounds of candy to the school kids every Christmas. Ask anyone, around Freeport, Jack Phillips was a good guy.

And in Flushing, where the Myrtle Avenue sewer assessment had to be paid, people like Carmine Scocca, Jacob Gescheidt and Mrs. Mary Brennan, were not likely to disagree. They had never heard of the wealthy Mr. Phillips, and did not connect him with their mortgaged homes or desperate struggles to get by.

Phillips was, however, well known in certain circles. He had been involved in the 1911 sewer scandal which had cost Borough President Gresser his job, paving the way for Connolly. An under-sheriff, one of the machine's "boys," he was not a pipe man then, but a culvert man and ward heeler. Phillips used to repair all kinds of culverts, even if he had to smash them first to make sure they needed repairing. Later on he discovered that it was not necessary to smash the culverts, he could merely send in his bill, saving everyone a good deal of bother.

He could hardly have been blamed for the one mistake he made in 1911, that of sending a bill for $422.80 for repairs on the plumbing of the Queens jail. A plumber later turned up who, having done the actual work, had been paid $115 by Phillips. Jack could not satisfactorily explain the $308.80 profit on this job, so a grand jury indicted him on nine different counts, including grand larceny. Somehow, he beat the charges.

He next turned up in 1914, having been accused of selling short weight and diseased meat to the public hospitals. He was a $4,000-a-year purchasing agent and he lasted until 1915, by which time so much overpriced, moldy beef had turned up in the county insane asylum that he was removed as "unfit, incompetent and lacking the necessary qualifications." He was also accused of trying to bribe a detective. No criminal charges were pressed.

Then in 1918, one Joseph L. Sigretto had a contract with the Lock-Joint Sewer Company as their agent in Queens. The contract was stolen from his safe by a man who later turned up in the employ of Phillips. Sigretto went to the company in an attempt to collect the $2,000 owed him, but was calmly informed that he wouldn't get a cent unless he could produce the contract. Of course Sigretto couldn't produce it, as it was already in the possession of Phillips. So Sigretto was now unable to buy any more Lock-Joint pipe. He quickly faded to nothingness as a contractor in Queens, while Phillips began his meteoric ascent.

But in 1927 Sigretto, as one of the triumvirate of undercutting contractors, returned to haunt the sewer ring. Interviewed in a Queens restaurant where he was eating spaghetti, Sigretto vowed to get even. "I am a Sicilian," he cried, brandishing his fork. "I shall make them pay."

Sigretto, in quoting these dramatic figures, promised a "new deal" for the people of Queens:

1925 Cost of Sewers *		1927 Figures *
3 ft. pipe	$90	$30
3 ft. 6 in. pipe	$90	$35
4 ft. 6 in. pipe	$110	$37
5 ft. 6 in. pipe	$148	$55

* per linear foot

The conduct of Borough President Connolly, caught with his fingers in the till, was, as the new year of 1927 dawned, erratic. Sometimes he would act blandly self-assured, but at other times he would become enraged. The night that Rice testified, Connolly sent sixty toughs to break up a meeting of the Allied Civic Associations, a meeting which, until the toughs arrived, resembled a college pep rally on the eve of the big game, its placards BEAT CONNOLLY instead of BEAT NOTRE DAME.

He was not giving up without a fight. On January 1, 1928, he arranged to have fifty prominent businessmen announce their support of him, while scoring Klein, Harvey and the others as "limelight seekers." And, being a lawyer, Connolly raised one legal obstruction after another to slow down proceedings against him. Evidently Phillips and the contractors who formed the sewer ring arranged certain other obstructions.

A supreme court justice, appointed by Governor Smith to conduct secret hearings, was challenged and forced out by Connolly on the grounds that the supreme court had no investigatory powers. Connolly also fought the secret hearings themselves. Through one legal maneuver after another, the hearings dragged on through the spring, at which time it was announced that they had cost the city $136,104. Whereupon a grand jury was handed the evidence and began deliberations: to indict or not to indict.

Meanwhile the extra-legal obstructions of the rest of the sewer ring might have been comical if the people involved hadn't been so patently crooked, and the citizens of Queens so deserving of justice.

Starting with the Awixa Corporation on January 4, 1928, the offices of one contractor after another were broken into by dastardly brigands and robbed. It seemed curious to everyone but the contractors themselves that nothing was missing from these "looted" offices except records of sewer construction in Queens, these same records being under supoena by the investigation. The police were always called in to verify the robbery, although sometimes several days late, and they often found fingerprints and other evidence to chase down, none of which ever led anywhere. This became known in court as "synthetic robbery."

Key witnesses, including good old Jack Phillips, also disappeared, even as process servers surrounded their homes, businesses and favorite haunts. Process servers and reporters kept watch twenty-four hours a day outside Phillips' house, an army that ruined his lawn and trampled his flowers. Once they spotted him on his glassed-in porch. Reporters rushed to the windows, holding up their hands to show that they concealed no subpoenas, stamping on tulips and iris beds in their eagerness to catch any utterance of the great man. "Phillips," wrote one reporter, "snapped his galluses at us with contempt, and stalked back into the house."

The Freeport police took steps to clear these mobs off Jack's property, harrying them on any pretext. One process server was arrested outside the driveway for reckless driving. "I was sitting in my parked car when this cop told me to move on," said the bewildered young man. "As soon as I started the car he turned on his siren. I stopped and he handed me a ticket for reckless driving."

As has been said, they liked Jack Phillips in Freeport.

For a while Phillips lived in Atlantic City, New Jersey, immune to New York State subpoenas. He used to return home every Sunday (it is against the law to serve a man on Sundays), but always was careful to leave before midnight. A regiment of process servers waited in the street, hoping he would overstay the witching hour. He never did.

Then for a while he dropped out of sight altogether. A chauffeur told reporters he was ill in a sanatorium outside the state. He was also said to be in Cuba, Florida and Montreal, but he turned up one day in February in a hotel in Newark, New Jersey, where his wife was receiving treatment for her feet —fallen arches.

Here Jack received reporters, his small eyes peering uncertainly from behind tortoise-rimmed glasses and a toupée crowning his normally bald head. The toupée was loose and slipped down toward his eyebrows every time he snapped his galluses with indignation, which was often. Jack would brush it negligently back into place.

"It's all right, Marion," he told his wife, "these young hounds have run me to earth, but I ain't got anything to say."

Whereupon, Jack discoursed for an hour.

Why did sewer pipe cost four to eight times more in Queens than anywhere else?

"I can't say that it does. I ain't never had a contract with the city in my life."

When had he last seen Connolly?

"I ain't seen that blankety-blank in seven or eight months."

Then you've had a falling-out?

"I ain't sore at him."

Then you're still good friends?

"We ain't never been good friends."

When water mains break they may spread destruction both above- and underground.

Will you tell us what you did with the $8,000,000 Henry Klein says you stole from the city?

"I'll give youse ninety-nine per cent of everything you find, so there's a chance to make some money."

What about your business?

"I ain't got any more business. They've ruined it. I ain't got any more pipe agency and I'm not sure I'll take it up again. I don't like to mix business with politics."

Sewer construction in Queens was at a standstill, and the water at some street corners was four feet deep. Residents organized themselves into labor battalions and dug great ditches through their lawns and gardens to make the water drain off toward the Sound.

On March 15, Connolly demanded that the city appropriate $100,000 for him to use as a defense fund. It was a bold stroke and it almost succeeded. Mayor Walker, not the most scrupulous of public officials, was more sympathetic now. "The fact that a man is accused of something is not going to drive me away from the support any man is entitled to. . . . The name of this city, its dignity and prestige is involved in these charges, and that should be upheld."

This raised such a furor that Walker was forced to backtrack the next day. "I meant that the city should bear the cost only if the accused is acquitted," the Mayor explained lamely.

Whereupon, Connolly resigned as Borough President, murmuring piously that he had done his best for the city and that, since his effectiveness was impaired by these charges, it was better that another man take over. He wished the fellow luck, whoever he would be.

Now the roof fell in, first on Phillips, then on Connolly. In Florida, Phillips suffered a kidney attack, brought on by too much whisky and the Federal Government's excessive interest in his income tax returns, which he had neglected to file every year since 1917. The tax men charged that he had earned $4,575,524 for 1925, 1926 and 1927, and owed $746,957. They could not go any further back than that because of the statute of limitations.

Phillips faced twenty-five years in jail and a $25,000 fine.

On March 31 he was indicted, and on April 7, still in the hospital, he was arrested by Federal agents. Tax liens had been attached to all his assets and his bail had to be furnished by a surety company.

About that same time, the New York State Legislature passed a law threatening witnesses who fled the state with a $100,000 penalty if they did not testify when under subpoena. Within hours of the passage of this bill, the missing witnesses in the sewer case began to trickle back to Queens. Even Phillips came back. He had lost his right kidney in an operation, he was pale and drawn and supported himself on a heavy walking stick, and he stopped off a few days in Jersey to have his teeth yanked, but he was back.

The grand jury began deliberations on May 8. Truckloads of records were brought to the courthouse, where armed guards watched them day and night. But nobody watched the jurors, one of whom reported that a fifty-five-year-old man, five feet six inches tall, with gray hair and eyes, wearing a gray fedora and carrying a brown suitcase—had offered him a bribe. The long-suffering Queens police carefully noted down this description, which sounded like and proved to be another wild-goose chase.

On June 22, the grand jury handed down the indictments: Connolly, Phillips, a consulting engineer named Clifford B. Moore, and Frederick Seely, engineer in charge of design in the Queens sewer bureau, on three counts of conspiracy.

Connolly, his short, rotund figure clad in a dark brown, pin-striped suit, held his hat behind his back and nervously turned its brim as he heard the indictment. When reporters confronted him later, he declared that he welcomed the indictment as a chance to clear his name: "As I have been without reproach, I do not fear it."

Phillips was not in court to hear himself indicted. He was ill in an Atlantic City hotel. His doctor announced that Jack's kidney ailment had turned worse, and that he was fighting off a coma. Almost nobody believed this. Old Jack was probably just lying low for a while. He'd come forward when it suited him, not before.

But on July 3, 1928, at three o'clock in the afternoon, millionaire Jack Phillips, the Pipe King, suddenly died. Uremia, said the doctor. But reporters kept prodding him and finally the physician admitted the true cause of death: alcoholism. Phillips had refused to keep to the strict diet which had been ordered, following his operation, and so he was dead.

His funeral was a grand affair, one of the social events of the season in Freeport. There was a Solemn High Requiem Mass at the Church of the Holy Redeemer. The Spanish War Veterans were there, and five hundred Elks, and the taxi drivers who would receive no more $20 tips, and the kids from the baseball team, and Father O'Toole, who told what a fine man Jack had been and read the place where it says: "Judge not, that you shall not be judged."

The cortege extended several blocks and was a long time reaching the cemetery. The casket was draped with an American flag; a bugler and firing squad had come from Fort Totten. Now in the bright, sunny afternoon, Father O'Toole read the burial prayer, taps rang out, loud and clear; the firing squad raised its rifles and a single barrage split the air. Then the mortal remains of Jack Phillips, the Pipe King, were slid into the mausoleum.

It was a sad occasion for his plump blond wife, Marion. Not only was Jack gone, but the tax men had tied up his money, and the will provided that Francis, his son by a previous marriage, should get almost all of it, if there was any left.

Reporters interviewed her through the screen door of her home. It was dusk and the Japanese servants seemed to have fled.

"I talked to him on the telephone the night before he died," Marion said. "I've talked to him many times when he was drunk and when he was sober, and that night he was sober. I was shocked the next day to hear of his death."

Marion demanded a full-scale investigation of his death, and for a while evidence leaned toward the theory that Jack had been done in by person or persons unknown. But it seemed that the police didn't care too much, one way or another, and in time the investigation was abandoned.

Meanwhile, Connolly continued hard at work obstructing justice. Even as four groups of Queens citizens were negotiating with the Borough President's office to construct their own private sewers (in lieu of public sewers paid for by the usual staggeringly high assessments), Connolly was demanding that his trial be postponed until after the election. The "inflammatory literature" handed out by Queens candidates in "this bitter political campaign" would be prejudicial to a fair trial, he charged.

When this motion was denied, Connolly attacked the indictment against him, the three separate charges of conspiracy which, together, added up to a felony and a possible long jail sentence. His argument was convincing. There was only one conspiracy involved, he maintained, so how could there be three charges.

Somebody had goofed. When the smoke cleared, Connolly was standing in court with only one charge outstanding, and that a misdemeanor. Barring sensational new evidence, Connolly figured to get off lightly. The trial was scheduled to start September 25, 1928, one of the key witnesses to be a sanitation engineer named William D'Olier, who had already been subpoenaed. D'Olier, who had done $1,600,000 worth of work on the sewers, evidently knew where the body was buried; in any case he was not permitted to reach the witness box.

His corpse was found just inside the railing of the Mount Zion Cemetery, Maspeth, Long Island, on September 2, a quiet place on a quiet Sunday morning. It was lying on its back on a slope, head downward, a .32 calibre revolver lightly clasped in the right hand, a neat little hole in the right temple. The police labeled it suicide, even though D'Olier's coat was torn in two places and the gun hand lay across his breast—hardly a likely position in the case of a man who had died instantly from a shot in the head.

The coat had probably been torn in removing the body to the morgue, said the police, defending their position. The interne who had pronounced D'Olier dead was produced; he claimed to have found the gun on the ground beside the body. He had placed it on the breast so that it wouldn't be overlooked by police, and had pressed the fingers around the handle so the gun wouldn't fall off and slide down the slope into the bushes

Perhaps, testified the lawyer of the dead man. But D'Olier had appeared badly frightened for a week before his death, and had once mumbled, relative to the sewer scandal: "Somebody's going to get bumped off before this thing is over." Another time, D'Olier had spoken of going to a meeting of Queens sewer contractors at which a fund was raised to induce someone to change his testimony.

Elvina D'Olier, wife of the deceased, took one look at the pistol which had killed her husband and declared innocently that it was not the gun he usually carried.

Connolly was questioned. "I met D'Olier through a client ten weeks ago," he said. No, Connolly had not seen him since.

A taxi driver swore that he had seen D'Olier and Connolly together twice within the past two weeks, that on each occasion he had driven D'Olier from his meeting with Connolly to some other spot.

A grand jury decided that D'Olier had been murdered. There was no evidence (and none ever developed) as to who had done it; particularly when the taxi driver suddenly changed his testimony. He had not seen Connolly and D'Olier together at all; he had probably seen D'Olier with someone who looked like Connolly, he said.

And so on September 25, 1928, after approximately $8,000,-000 had been stolen from the people of Queens, after one man had been murdered and another was dead under suspicious circumstances, the trial of ex-Borough President Maurice E. Connolly and ex-Engineer Fred Seely, on charges of misdemeanor, got ponderously under way. (Consultant Moore was tried separately for state income tax infractions only.)

It lasted just twenty-one days. Seely made almost no defense, largely because there seemed to be no case against him. Connolly tried hard to knock the props from under the principal evidence brought forward by the prosecution, which was that he had been involved in twenty-three transactions with fourteen different persons between October 1, 1925, and November 19, 1927, and that he had spent in cash $145,454, his salary being $15,000 a year. It did not help Connolly that his home (paid for in cash) was valued at $81,138, or that he was the owner of five safe-deposit boxes under various names, or that he belonged to the swank Prospect Gun and Rod Club at Freeport where, during the trial, he spent his weekends fishing.

The case went to the jury just past midday on October 16. For reporters and spectators the afternoon dragged slowly by. Night fell, and rumors began circulating that the jury was hung, the vote being 11 to 1 for conviction. This surprised no one. Connolly was too slippery, and the anguished Borough of Queens fully expected to see him go scot-free.

At length Judge Arthur S. Tompkins permitted the jury to retire for the night; heavily chaperoned, they were led away to the Kew Gardens Inn. Tompkins himself had a bed made up in his chambers and slept there.

In the morning deliberations began again. It was one o'clock when the jury announced that it had reached a verdict. Court was hastily reconvened and the prisoners brought in. Since Connolly and Seely were being tried on misdemeanor charges only, they were not obliged to stand and face the jury.

But from their chairs both men searched the faces of their peers, hoping for some sign of approval. The jurors were stony-faced, and Connolly turned away, looking for the first time like a beaten man. Seely still held out hope for himself. Perhaps the jury would convict one and free the other; and of course he had a better chance of getting off than Connolly.

"Gentlemen of the jury, have you reached a verdict?" asked Judge Tompkins.

Answered the foreman: "We find the defendants guilty as charged!"

An excited buzz filled the courtroom. Connolly's short pudgy figure slumped forward. His face, always so highly colored as to indicate high blood pressure, seemed to turn purple, and his eyes blinked. Seely's long thin face turned white, and his lips twitched uncontrollably.

Before hearing his sentence Seely, in a husky voice made this plea to the court: "By reason of my conviction my reputation is gone and my life is ruined. I will be unable in the future to earn a livelihood. I have spent over half my life in the service of the city and the construction of public works. I ask the court for leniency."

Connolly, whose ambition as a young man had been to become a supreme court justice, said nothing.

"I am very sorry for you Mr. Seely," said Judge Tompkins, after a moment, "but I cannot show any discrimination between you and Mr. Connolly." Maximum sentence was imposed, a year's imprisonment and a $500 fine.

Connolly, forty-eight, and Seely, fifty-one, spent the night in jail, sending out in the morning for stewed apricots, ham and eggs, toast and coffee. After two days, both men were sprung, their attorneys having filed appeals. Connolly promptly sailed for Europe. Reporters interviewed him at the pier, where he announced that he would be back in a few weeks and was confident of eventual vindication.

Oddly enough, he did come back. His first appeal was rejected and so was his second. All of this took time. It was not until May 9, 1930, that Connolly and Seely were finally obliged to give themselves up. Seely arrived inconspicuously at Welfare Island, between Queens and Manhattan, where sentence was to be served. To the reporters who awaited him he said, "Although I have been unjustly convicted, I lack the funds to continue the fight." He was admitted inside the prison.

Connolly arrived in his chauffeur-driven limousine, ducking the press by taking a different ferry than had been expected. The guard at the gate reached in the window to shake Connolly's hand. Inside he was warmly greeted by Warden Joseph McCann. By this time reporters and photographers swarmed around him, snapping his picture, firing questions.

"Why make a Mardi Gras of it?" demanded Connolly sulkily.

Then for a while the press forgot about them, except for reporting Connolly's attack of influenza, and wondering whether his wife and daughter "who usually go to Europe this time of year," would go without Dad.

A year's sentence was little enough, considering the amount of money stolen, but both Connolly and Seely were granted two months off for good behavior and were released March 4, 1931. Seely immediately dropped out of sight. Not so Connolly, who, looking tanned and fit, was met by his chauffeur at seven in the morning and driven home, the car skidding across his lawn in its efforts to avoid hitting reporters who jumped in front of it.

Aside from remarking that he was considering writing a book on his prison experiences, Connolly refused to talk to the press. A little later he sent a maid to the door with a statement. Since the trial had taken place in the middle of a bitter political campaign, Connolly wrote, the public was so aroused that calm judgment was impossible. "I ask no sympathy and my political enemies and others involved in my prosecution, some of them grossly misled, are entitled to all the satisfaction they can get out of the fact that they have accomplished, under legal form, the conviction of an innocent man."

Connolly settled down to live the life of a country squire, ministered to by servants, a man of leisure, while in the poorer sections of Queens men began to mutter about justice. It was true that Seely was a ruined man but look—just look—at the fat, ex-Borough President. He was rich, his health was perfect. . . . Whereupon, Connolly was felled by a stroke, then a second one. On November 24, 1935, at the age of fifty-four, the third stroke killed him. It was four and a half years since he had retired from jail, politics and public life, to enjoy his ill-gotten gains.

So ended the great sewer scandal, a neat little story with everything wrapped up except the whereabouts of $8,000,000 and the identity of a murderer.

Did the good people of Queens learn anything from this soul-searing experience?

They most emphatically did not.

On August 19, 1952, after residents complained of foul odors emanating from sewers, Borough President James A. Lundy climbed down into a two-mile, $185,679 stretch of new pipe and found that the seams had been calked with old newspapers and rags. Thus, twenty-five years after the first sewer scandal broke, the Borough of Queens had another. This trial was to last 202 days; at the end of it, two contractors and three city inspectors would receive jail terms up to eight and a half years.

At least this time nobody got shot.

16. King of the Sewers

As LONG AS THERE are sewers in New York, the men who work them will talk about Teddy May—of how he knew sewers so well that he could look at a manhole cover and tell you exactly where the break was; of how he once plunged into a flooded sewer to drag out a half-drowned comrade; of how he tracked down murder weapons, loot and other evidence which had been tossed into sewers, then gave testimony in court that put dozens of crooks behind bars; of how, during his hundreds of court appearances as expert witness in both criminal and civil cases, he used to shout or growl at attorneys, juries and even judges as if they were sewer workers. Teddy May put on airs for no man.

Teddy always carried a potato in his pocket because he believed a potato warded off back pains, and his clothes were stained with tobacco juice—he had been chewing since he was nine—but for over fifty years he was as much Mayor (albeit a crude and despotic one) under the streets of New York, as Jimmy Walker, Fiorello La Guardia, Robert Wagner and others were Mayor upon them.

He was uneducated and uncouth, but generals, police commissioners and other prominent men were anxious to do him favors, and it is said that he became a political figure capable of making or breaking surrogates and aldermen.

Teddy May was a little man, not much over five feet two. His voice was loud and rasping, his speech picturesque and his grammar atrocious, but he knew every turn and joint of New

York's 560 miles of sewers. The sewers were his domain, one
he guarded jealously, and he reigned below ground like a king.

From 1903 when Teddy made the first survey of the sewer
system, until about 1940, the only map of the network was the
one Teddy carried in his head. He also had the only topographical map of the original island, showing where the marsh
ground had been, and where twenty-one streams still burbled
on under countless tons of asphalt and concrete. Late in life
he at last admitted where this map had come from. He had
"hooked it out of the department."

This knowledge Teddy held like a cocked revolver at the
head of the city, protecting his power. Thus for half a century
no new sewers were laid in New York, nor old ones condemned,
without the approval of Teddy May. During the twenty-nine
years he was Superintendent of Sewers he was on call twenty-
four hours a day. Whenever a main exploded or sprang a leak,
endangering lives or property, Teddy would take personal
charge at the scene, working tirelessly, ignoring danger, his
loud rasp of a voice ringing out above the tumult, gradually
smothering the chaos which had existed before he got there.

For his Napoleonesque manner he was unpopular with his
men. "Chew-tobacco Teddy" they called him, though not to
his face. Having only a few teeth, he chewed with his gums.
He had no control over his right eyelid, either. It hung half
shut like a broken shade. He got the bad eye one icy cold
day in 1925 when a steam line broke. Teddy crawled in to fix
it, the steam blowing off at three hundred degrees. When he
climbed outside again the temperature was nine degrees and
the change, said Teddy, paralyzed his right lid.

"Lost four days in fifty-one years on the job because of the
eye," he once growled. "It closes up in the winter, but it
never bothers me except when I chew tobacco on my right side
and I miss and it hits my coat."

Teddy growled at everybody, even at Mayor La Guardia,
another small man with a loud voice. "If you were in the same
room with them," recalled one associate, "Teddy would make
you think La Guardia was an imbecile." It was the same in
court. Teddy's testimony could not be questioned. He would
fix even the judge in the steely glare of his one good eye and

rasp, "What the hell do you know about it?" Juries believed him; no complainant ever obtained a judgment against the city after Teddy had taken the stand. Teddy saved the city "an incalculable amount of money," according to James P. Lundy, who succeeded him as superintendent in 1954. "The city used Teddy May and his knowledge for years," declared General John Reed Kilpatrick, President of Madison Square Garden.

Teddy May carried all his information in his head, developing a fantastic memory because he had had little education and could scarcely scrawl an intelligible sentence. "I didn't pay too blankety much attention in school," he said once. "I was alluz on the hook." He kept a secretary to type up his reports, and a cuspidor in the bottom drawer of his desk so that he could dictate in comfort.

In his time, Teddy had crawled or swum through every navigable foot of the sewer network. He knew every trouble spot, he knew where dropwells plunged down thirty feet to pass under subways, he knew where the amazing brick sewers of colonial times were now handling the waste of skyscrapers. He knew where to find the almost nine thousand catch basins and time and again the police came to him for help.

One time there was a cop who claimed he had lost his shield and so was issued another one. Later the cop resigned from the force, turned in the second shield and began using the first one to extort money from shopkeepers. When things got too hot for him, the ex-cop tossed the shield in a sewer. Teddy May traced it through a labyrinth of pipes to a certain catch basin. When the shield was produced against him in court, the ex-cop went white from the shock. He also went to Sing Sing for ten years where, no doubt, he brooded about the fickleness of sewers and the persistence of Teddy May.

Another time Teddy cracked an insurance swindle. "These broads would climb out of a cab, flash a piece of fake jewelry, then make as if it slipped out of their hands. Naturally there's a sewer under where they're standing, and a couple of suckers passing by who don't know no better than to make out affidavits sayin' they seen the ice fall into the sewer. The broad then tries to collect on the insurance, and the insurance company calls me. I find the fake diamonds and the broad winds up in the clink."

Teddy, who had found a score or more of guns too, was contemptuous of the criminal mind. "Them bums think they're gettin' rid of a hot item when they throw it down a sewer. They don't know it only travels a few feet."

His job sometimes called for shrewd detective work of another kind. Once, in a sewer on West Street, Teddy's men began keeling over, one by one. Teddy ordered the sewer evacuated. Four men had been overcome, and one later died.

What had caused it? Was it a new kind of odorless sewer gas? Teddy traced the sewer to a point beneath a cleaning establishment. The cleaners had used an acid to purge its vats, then dumped the residue into the sewer. On contact with the sewer water, the acid had become a lethal fog.

Teddy May seemed to know everybody, and no one who ever met him could forget Teddy. Small, one eye half shut, with a loud voice and a cheek full of chewing tobacco, he knew he was a character and made the most of it. Under the gaze of pedestrians peering into one of his excavations, he would begin to stride mysteriously about, barking orders like Napoleon himself.

He was fond of giving salty speeches at union or political meetings, peppering the air with Teddy Mayisms. Linoleum, to Teddy was "rinoleum," and he sometimes spoke also of "sympathy" orchestras, "horowitzers," and of two men "getting between ya."

The extent of Teddy's influence, or how he had come by it in the first place, was never clearly defined. General Kilpatrick always sent him tickets to Garden events, because, explained Teddy, "when they were building the Garden I showed them how to fix the drains on that flat roof. Otherwise they would have flooded the joint every time it rained."

Other contacts were more mysterious, like the Police Commissioner during the thirties who, with an almost religious fervor, was engaged in breaking inefficient and dishonest cops. This Commissioner was so fierce that even the Mayor was said to be afraid of him. He was considered unapproachable.

One day a cop, call him O'Toole, came to Teddy for help.

The cop had slugged his lieutenant for a reputed insult, and his days on the force appeared numbered.

He asked Teddy to introduce him to the police chaplain, a personal friend of Teddy. Like Teddy, O'Toole had once been a bricklayer, and Teddy now took pity on him.

Teddy fixed the cop with his gimlet eye.

"Ya ever been in trouble before?"

"I swear to God," said O'Toole.

"That priest can't help you," said Teddy. "But if you want, I'll go down and talk to the Commissioner for you."

Forthwith, Teddy got on the subway and went to see the Commissioner. Admitted to the office of the man feared throughout the city, Teddy began by declaring: "O'Toole ain't never been in trouble before."

"That's what you think," said the Commissioner, and he began reading a long list of complaints against O'Toole.

"Okay, okay," interrupted Teddy, "so the kid's my cousin. What can you do for him?"

"Your cousin," said the Commissioner. "That's different. Why didn't you say so in the first place?"

O'Toole got off with fifteen days' suspension from duty. A few weeks later Teddy ran into the Commissioner at a prize fight.

"How'd your cousin make out?" asked the Commissioner.

"What are you asking me for?" rasped Teddy, who hadn't troubled to find out, "you're the Commissioner, ain't ya?"

Edward Patrick May was born on Forty-second Street and Tenth Avenue on May 5, 1874, so he claimed, or perhaps in Ireland a little earlier than that. There was no trace of brogue in his accent, which was strictly Hell's Kitchen, but his bricklayer's card was the only document he ever cared to produce, even when he had passed retirement age and was seeking a waiver to stay on duty.

Son of a foundry worker, Teddy was the fifth of eleven children. As a boy he was sent to every school from Fourteenth to Fifty-ninth streets.

"If they didn't put me out, I ran out. We liked to wait for the truant officer and slam him over the head. Then we'd lead him a wild chase across the top of the freight cars."

At thirteen, Teddy May ran out once and for all, going to work in the foundry with his father. A little later he worked in a carpet factory, then became a bricklayer. That was 1890, and his first job was working on the Astor mansion on Fifth Avenue.

He was twenty-four when the Spanish-American War started. He tried to join the army.

"But I was short of teeth and height. So I sends a substitute to take the examination and the next day I'm in uniform. Wore it all of ten days when the Colonel saw me standing and talking and fires me clean out of the army."

By 1903 Teddy was making sixty-five cents an hour as a bricklayer. Then a lockout tied up construction for seventeen weeks, and Teddy and a pal decided to take off for Baltimore where, it was said, a good bricklayer could make eighty cents an hour. The two were on their way when Teddy got a call from Borough President Camden's office.

"We need a good man in the sewers," said Mr. Camden. "You've been recommended by the bricklayers' union."

Teddy went to work for Chief Engineer Harris Loomis the next day. Teddy was a small man, one who, presumably, would fit into a small pipe, and Loomis suggested he chart the entire sewer system—no chart existed at the time.

So Teddy set out to explore every foot of the sewers. In those days many sewers were nothing more than wooden barrels, some so slippery that Teddy would have to kick off his boots and swim for it. Others were broad as a truck and made of fine blue stone which glimmered faintly in the dim light.

Six years passed before he had finished—and there was still no chart of the sewers. Teddy kept it all in his head. But if there was no chart, there was at least one man who knew more about the system than any other man. Teddy May had become an expert on sewers. He made the most of it.

He was never uncertain and he was always mysterious. When called to the scene of a leak, he would gaze at heaven as if seeking inspiration, then plunge in and find the break. Men marveled at his knowledge and memory. Success followed success.

Nor did it hurt Teddy's career when, in 1910, he helped recover a $25,000 black diamond ring which General Grant's daughter lost in the plumbing of the old King's Hotel on West Forty-third Street. The ring was a keepsake of inestimable value—it had been presented to her by the Emperor of Japan when she was married in the White House.

The ring had been insured by Lloyd's of London, whose inspectors questioned the janitor of the building. This man claimed that he had searched the traps but had found nothing.

Lloyd's called in Teddy May.

First Teddy examined the traps, found a lot of rusty beer caps there, and concluded that the janitor, if he had looked hard, would have removed the caps. Next he had Lloyd's make a paste duplicate of the ring and, in the presence of detectives, proved that it could not flushed away.

"I'm highly suspicious of such goings on as this," he then observed. "If you ask me, it's an inside job," and he gestured significantly toward the janitor's quarters.

What happened?

"So the Lloyd's guy becomes a fireman in the hotel," Teddy was fond of reporting, "watches the janitor, and finds the diamond in the janitor's locker."

At recovering articles lost in sewer catch basins, Teddy was, from the start, an artist. "It may take a little time and a lot of flushing," he used to say, "but if it's in there it will be where I said it was when I go to look for it."

Once he found a paper box containing $35,000 in negotiable securities. It seems a real estate office had been cleaned out by stick-up men who had imagined the bonds worthless and so had dumped them. Another time he recovered a man's teeth.

On this particular night the phone rang at 3:00 A.M.

"Lishen," said a voice thickly, "thish ish an emergency. I jush losh my teesh. Ya gotta help me."

"Yer what?" demanded Teddy groggily.

"My teesh. I was walkin' acrosh the street tryin' to stop hiccupin' an' all of a sudden I belched and my plate shot out of my moush down a sewer. Ya gotta help me. I can't go home wishout my teesh. My wife will kill me."

"Where are you?" demanded Teddy.

A few minutes later, Teddy drove up to the spot, a saloon. Inside was the toothless drunk.

"I jush been sittin' here waitin'," this individual explained.

Teddy, who never drank, sniffed the air disgustedly. "That ain't all ya been doing. Where's the sewer?"

It was a warm, quiet night in June and so late that the city was soundless. Noisily, Teddy pried up the manhole cover, plunged into the sewer and reappeared a few minutes later with the dentures in his fist. The drunk, according to Teddy, "yanks his teeth out of my hand, washes them at the pump, shoves them in his mouth and runs off home."

Recovering objects from sewers was a consistent headache to Teddy. "Only about twenty-five things a year have any real value," he used to say. "We get a lot of women yellin' they lost valuable jewelry. Liars. They go gamblin' and tell their husbands they lost it, but they hocked it to gamble some more!"

Teddy May never was bothered by false modesty; always growled his true feelings and thus completely antagonized some people.

"There was this borough president in La Guardia's time," he remembered. "He had a sore against me. He had been a contractor building on West Street in marsh ground and I told him to be careful he didn't undermine the sewers because if he did he'd be pumping there from now to doomsday. He wouldn't listen to me because he was from, you know, Massachusetts Tech. Well, he caved in thirty-five feet of sewers on that job, and twenty-six feet more on another job on Twelfth Avenue which I also warned him about, so they made him Borough President and he made up the budget that year and one of my friends warned me that he had cut me $1,100."

Teddy appealed first to the bricklayers' union, then to Mayor La Guardia. At this time La Guardia was examining the books of contractors, and he had broken some 250 city inspectors after finding their names on the contractors' books as recipients of "gifts."

In response to Teddy's appeal, La Guardia "said I was the most honestest man in the city and he put the eleven hundred back and three hundred more besides."

Another time, Teddy entered the office of a borough president, seeking raises for some of his men. The sewer man's plea was as graphic as it was ungrammatical, and when it was finished the Borough President remarked: "It's easy to see that you are a keen student of the English language."

The sarcasm was not lost on Teddy.

"I'll tell you who I am," he snapped. "I'm the guy who carries the cripples and old ladies down the fire escapes to the polls to vote to put bums like you in office. That's who I am."

Valuable as he was to the city, Teddy May never earned more than $7,000 a year, or wanted to. As he approached that figure he began to refuse raises. The sewers were his life and he was afraid some "big shot" might force him out if the job was made too rewarding.

He had a wife and daughter at home, but spent little time there. It was sewers that he loved. He always referred to them as "she," and spoke of them fondly. Sewers normally are odorless, and Teddy had no patience with those who supposed sewers stink. "Sewers smell better than you do," he'd retort, thrusting a grimy finger in the man's face. He defended sewer manhole covers from the charge of being noisy under traffic: "It's the utility covers that make all the noise; we call them clankers."

When a bartender descended to his wine cellar with a lighted candle intending to draw a bung—and set off a pocket of gas which leveled three-quarters of a block, Teddy had no sympathy at all. "They blamed it on sewer gas," he said. "It wasn't sewer gas at all, it was a leaky gas main."

Once, Department of Sanitation plows, cleaning up after a blizzard, began pushing the refuse impregnated snow down open manholes. Teddy took it as a personal insult. Rushing to the office of Hugo L. Rogers, then Borough President, he screamed: "Make them stop shoveling that stuff into my sewers, or I quit!" Rogers ordered the problem of the snow solved some other way. "No one knows the sewers like Teddy," he said. "Suppose he did quit. What would we do then?"

Age did not temper Teddy May. At seventy-nine he was named to a fund-raising committee by the pastor of Holy Cross Church on Forty-second Street, where Teddy had served as an usher for thirty-three years, and as President of the Holy Name Society for seventeen.

"I went in and told him, 'Father, I'm seventy-nine years of age, I ain't gonna climb them stairs, get somebody else.'"

A few days later, Teddy reported to the rectory with his own contribution to the drive, $125 in cash.

"That's a lot of money for a working man," Teddy later recalled. "But I wanted him to take that much for now. Then if the drive fell short, I'd give more later."

But the pastor, according to Teddy, spurned the donation, saying, "We don't need your money, you're a big shot."

Which caused Teddy to scream: "How much you giving, Father? You got two jobs, chaplain of the cops and you work here. You don't pay no board, neither. How much you giving? You're a Catholic too, ain't ya?"

And from then on, when Teddy wanted to go to church, he walked down to Holy Innocents on Thirty-seventh Street.

Finally, at eighty, against his will, Teddy May did retire. The date was June 2, 1954. His hair was white, his neck shriveled up inside his collar, but he was still spry. There was a little party for him in the sewer department office, he was sworn in as Honorary Commissioner of Sewers by Hulan Jack, Borough President, and was presented with a gold badge designating this rank. Teddy was filled with pride about the badge, but would never admit it: "All it's good for is I can get into the race track free with it," he used to say, showing it to people on the slightest provocation.

Teddy May in his prime was a jealous, suspicious person. He was loud and crude, he was terribly strict with his daughter when she was growing up, and he was tightfisted with his money: "Teddy wouldn't spend a nickle to see the Statue of Liberty fall over," is the way one man phrased it.

But for all that, Teddy would help any man he could. "It's impossible to know how much good Teddy has done," said one who knew him well, "or how many hundreds of people are in his debt." For instance, he used his connection with the Garden to bring gangs of slum youngsters to rodeos and circuses; he drove the Holy Cross nuns around in his car on Sundays, Teddy crouched over the wheel, the nuns sitting primly upright, the car plainly stenciled: *DEPARTMENT OF SEWERS;* and he helped General Kilpatrick find a stream which runs under the Garden, which the Garden hoped to funnel into its air conditioning. On this occasion he even lent the General his topographical map, a far greater sacrifice than one who did not know Teddy could possibly believe: "It was like giving away his arm," said one associate.

As this is written Teddy May is eighty-four years old and only a shadow of the man he used to be. He does not have much to do. Sometimes he goes to the race track. Mostly he sits in the sun on the steps along Forty-second Street, chatting with oldtimers who pass by, his hands folded on his knees, spreading them eight or ten inches every few seconds to squirt a jet of tobacco juice down onto the pavement. Everybody around there knows Teddy. He does not talk much about the old days.

They will be sad around the sewer department when Teddy May goes, because there can never be such a man again. Bookish types staff the sewer department today. The department—and the world—is in the hands of the graduate engineers and there is no longer room for the Teddy Mays. He is the last of his kind. He learned the job not in books but by crawling through the pipes. He took that job, which some considered beneath the dignity of a man, and from it extracted prestige, excitement, success, even glamour—which is what all men yearn for in their work, but which only a few lucky ones ever find. It might be said that the sewers ennobled Teddy May, and he them.

Those who knew Teddy will remember him and tell stories about him; about the time, for instance, when Teddy was fixing a sewer outside the swank Hotel Pierre, while a society wedding, presided over by a glistening white, eight-foot-high wedding cake guarded by a proud French chef, progressed in the ballroom inside.

At length, sweaty and grimy, Teddy crawled out of the sewer and headed for the hotel boiler room. On the way, the lavish wedding caught his eye, the frock coats of the men, the ladies' bejeweled gowns. Teddy always was partial to dramatic en-

New York Telephone Company.

In the old days broken telephone cable was repaired with hot lead carried underground in a modest container.

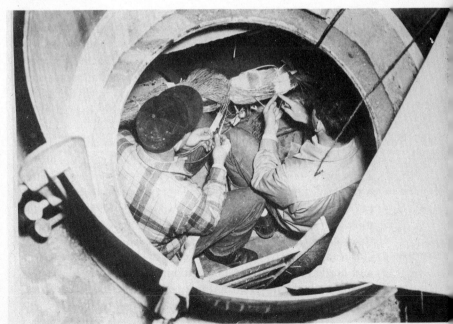

Platnick's Photo Service

Telephone men at work on their "delicate wires" beneath the streets today.

trances, and now he made one. Across the ballroom he strode, looking like—like a man who had just crawled out of a sewer—making straight for the giant cake. The festive blue bloods watched aghast as, brushing the French chef aside, he dragged a filthy finger across the pristine whiteness of the cake and plunged a big gob of icing into his mouth. Then he fixed the stunned crowd with his good eye.

"Hmmm, good!" he said.

That was Teddy May.

17. Alligators in the Sewers

ALLIGATORS, small boys and at least one horse have accidentally swum in the sewers of New York. The boys and the horse seem not to have enjoyed the experience, but the alligators throve on it.

Sewer inspectors first reported seeing alligators about 1935, Teddy May being Superintendent at the time. Neither May nor anyone else believed them.

"I says to myself," May recalled, "them guys been drinking in there." He refused to approve reports mentioning alligators. Instead, he set men to watch the sewer walkers to find out how they were obtaining whisky down in the pipes, and where they hid it when off duty.

Before long Teddy's checkers reported that there was no evidence of clandestine booze below decks, but that inspectors were still claiming narrow escapes from alligators.

"I'll go down there and prove to youse guys that there ain't no alligators in my sewers," rasped Teddy.

A chastened Teddy May returned to his office a few hours later. Had he been a drinking man, he would have poured himself a stiff one. He sat at his desk screwing his fists into his eyes, trying to forget the sight of alligators serenely paddling around in his sewers. The beam of his own flashlight had spotlighted alligators whose length, on the average, was about two feet. Some may have been longer. Avoiding the swift current of the trunk lines under major avenues, the beasts had wormed up the smaller pipes under less important neighborhoods, and there Teddy had found them. The colony appeared to have settled contentedly under the very streets of the busiest city in the world.

Teddy could not comprehend how they had got there and, though he wouldn't admit it, he did not know how to get rid of them.

Various sewer inspectors advanced their own theories about the origin of the anachronistic reptiles. The most plausible was this: During those years painted turtles had become a fad among youngsters, and nearly every boy or girl had a bowl or tank in the house containing a "collection."

Because turtles sold so well, dealers began to import their distant cousins, lizards, salamanders and even alligators, riding the fad for all it was worth. Now turtles, lizards and salamanders do not grow much and, handled roughly by children, die rather easily. But the recently hatched alligators, shipped up from Florida in tiny perforated boxes, grew and grew and grew until the bowls and tanks which contained them were too small. At Junior's insistence, the residence of the friendly 'gator was thereupon transferred to the family bathtub, only the 'gator wasn't too friendly any more, and Dad had grown extremely nervous about lifting him out every time anyone wanted to bathe. Also, those were depression times and the voracious appetites of the beasts became a bit nerveracking too.

As the days passed, Father grew madder and madder. Junior's tears would not be able to save his pet much longer.

Finally the breaking point came. Either the alligator went, or Father went.

Having reached this decision, a new problem arose. How does one kill a two-foot alligator—you can't stuff a live one in a garbage can. Various ways were considered and, in most cases, discarded. Poison was difficult to obtain, expensive, and a risk with children around the house. Besides, who would hold Junior while a wad of strychnine was rammed down the throat of his "friend."

No one wanted to use a knife on the beast. Merely to touch it was repulsive to most parents, who hardly relished the prospect of sawing through that armor.

So parents adopted the easiest way. One night after Junior

was in bed, Father rushed into the bathroom, grabbed the alligator by the tail and, teeth bared insanely now, darted out into the street, straight for the corner sewer. His strength increased tenfold by the emotion of the moment, Dad dug two fingers under the manhole cover and whipped it aside. With a plop, the alligator disappeared.

Dad's feeling of release, as he walked back to the house, was ecstatic. The hated alligator, so he thought, was gone forever.

Within a day or two of admitting that there really were alligators in his sewers, Teddy May was able to face the problem of eliminating them.

A few months later they were gone. Some succumbed to rat poison. Others were harassed by sewer inspectors into swimming into the trunk mains, where the Niagara-like current washed them out to sea. Some were drowned when blockages filled their secluded pipes with backwash—to the very top. And a few were hunted down by inspectors with .22 rifles and pistols—not as part of the job, but as sport—possibly the most unusual hunting on earth, a veritable sewer safari.

Boys in the sewers have, over the years, been a good deal more commonplace than alligators. Most fall in while trying to fish balls out, and if they go under at all it usually means tragedy, for they are sucked into pipes and drowned. Teddy May once directed an all-night search for one lad, while floodlights illuminated the manhole and the crowd was held back by ropes. Both the police and weeping parents beseeched him to find the boy, who was believed lodged in the neck of a pipe. Teddy got the boy out all right, but too late.

One seven-year-old was luckier. He came upon an open manhole at Fifty-third Street and Third Avenue one evening, and began pitching in rocks. After each throw he would lean over listening for the splash. Then he leaned over too far and tumbled in.

Without so much as a scream, he disappeared. His playmates ran crying to their parents. The fire department sent men down into every sewer in the neighborhood; then, almost as an afterthought, stationed a man at Forty-ninth Street where the trunk line emptied into the East River. A few minutes later a small, black, mud-covered figure shot out of the pipe into the water. They fished the child out, filthy, but unharmed, having been flushed along half a mile under city streets by the swift sewer current.

"It was terrible cold in there," said the little boy. "No, I wasn't scared. I wasn't scared at all."

As for horses in the sewers, that has happened, so far as is known, only once. As the late New York *Times* columnist Meyer Berger told the story, it was forty years ago in a remote section of Brooklyn. Mr. Berger, a cub reporter then, was watching a construction job. A great dray horse was tugging away at a piece of machinery when suddenly the harness broke and the animal pitched forward into an open manhole.

It, too, disappeared in an instant, to the everlasting astonishment of the workmen and the consternation of that poor man, its owner, who hired it out for the day, and who counted it his only means of livelihood.

But wiser heads in the crowd began shouting: "To the river, to the river," and all raced in that direction, stationing themselves where the great trunk pipe poured its contents into New York Harbor. In a moment out poured the horse, a tangle of thrashing legs and rearing head. When it came to the surface it righted itself and, neighing frantically, paddled toward shore. It clambered up the bank, a most befuddled beast, according to Mr. Berger. Bits of sewage were stuck to its coat, but this did not deter its owner who ran up and kissed it anyway.

A great deal of money has been found in the sewers, particularly during the depression when WPA labor scraped out or rebuilt vast lengths of pipes on Manhattan's West Side. The current in New York's trunk mains is so swift that it will— well, it will wash along a horse. The trunk mains, therefore, are self-cleansing. But the branch lines drop only a quarter inch per foot, an incline so slight that the sewage moves slowly at best, and not at all at worst.

The sludge, which cakes on the bottom of branch mains, is what these desperately poor WPA workers were sent in to re-

move. To their absolute delight they found that the sludge was impregnated with coins. Hundreds of them. Thousands of them.

The regular procedure had been to chip loose slabs of sludge, load them into a pail, then yank on the rope attached to the pail, signaling topside that your pail was full. The men above would drag it out, empty it, and drop it down again. No one liked working in the sewers, but these were depression years and a man took what he could get. The crews alternated, four hours in the sewer, four hours outside emptying pails instead of filling them. A man outside felt himself an aristocrat, superior in every way to the moles under the street.

The discovery of gold changed all that. A piece of sludge broke apart in a man's hand exposing a quarter. Immediately he dived for the pail he had just filled and began to crush slabs of sludge in his fingers. He found a dime, a penny, another quarter. He went through the pail a second time, dumping its content out and stomping on it until it was pulverized. More coins turned up. He began to yell excitedly. Other men began searching *their* pails. They, too, found coins.

The men began to attack the sewer with frantic energy. When the next crew came to relieve them, they refused to go, shooing the others out of the tunnel. Soon the second crew, having discovered what was happening, clamored and fought to get down to the sludge.

The WPA had struck a vein that seemed as rich as the Klondike. Men staggered up to the street drunk with wealth, their pockets bulging with money. Gone were the previous social distinctions; the man in the sewer was a prospector (they called themselves "Klondikers"); the men who preferred outdoor work were fools.

The West Side sewers became the most sought-after work in town. Soon the men instituted a share-the-profits plan such as countermen in diners employ, and each man went below with two pails, one for sludge, one for coins. The sludge was "klondiked" once in the sewer, then sent aloft where it was "reklondiked." All the money was kept in a neat pile beside the manhole, to be divided at the end of the day. All day the men took pleasure watching the pile grow (some attained a height of two or more feet) and toward quitting time they loved the way it glinted in the descending sun.

Like other veins of gold, the one in the sewers gave out after a time. Sewer prospecting does not exist any more. The day of the "klondiker" is over.

Much political gold has been made in the sewers—or at least near them. Some years ago one G. D. Friou, campaigning for Alderman in Brooklyn on a platform of "Sewers That Work," came up with an odd stunt to impress his constituents.

It had rained for three days and some Brooklyn street corners were flooded. Friou drove up with a canoe on top of his car. It was launched by hip-booted party workers, Friou was helped aboard and he began to harangue the crowd which watched, grinning, from higher ground.

Three weeks later more rain backed up the sewers a second time. This time Friou drove up in a truck containing an elephant which he had borrowed from the Brighton Menagerie. His canoe was again launched and the elephant, with one blow of its trunk, sent Friou and the canoe skimming across the temporary pond and almost through a store window.

It was a televsion comedian named Art Carney who found the highest assay gold in New York's sewers. As everyone knows, Carney played a sewer worker opposite Jackie Gleason's bus driver in one of the most successful TV series of all time. Carney's sewer worker was an engaging simpleton, a man of ingratiating stupidity and monumental good will, and the whole country loved him.

Although Carney's character enjoyed the sewers so much that he even ate his lunch in there, Carney himself descended into a New York sewer only once.

Early in his role he contacted James P. Lundy, then Superintendent, and asked permission to examine at close hand one or two of the pipes he was spoofing.

Lundy took him to a manhole on the West Side. When the cover was removed, Carney could see nothing but a deep black hole filled with the sound of rushing water.

"Now a sewer, the first time you go in one, is a very spooky thing," is the way Lundy tells the story. "I was scared the first time I went in one, and now I could tell by his face that Art was a little nervous too."

Taking Carney by the arm and speaking in a serious tone, Lundy said: "Now, Art, I want you to be very, very careful. If you should slip you would plunge down thirty feet where a mile-a-minute current would catch you up, whisk you across under the island and out into the East River."

For a moment the comedian, worried, gazed at him. Then he dropped abruptly into the character of the sewer worker he played on TV. He pushed the brim of his hat up, gave an idiot chuckle and said: "That's okay, I live over on that side of town anyway."

Actually, the sewers Carney's TV character talked about bore little resemblance to those under the streets of New York, filled as they were with ledges on which the men played poker ("wet cards wild") while the sewer current rushed by inches away. The sewers of Paris are like that, but the sewers of New York are more often smooth-bored, oval-shaped, vitrified concrete pipe—terribly practical, though admittedly a bit prosaic.

18. The Most Delicate Wires

When the Erie barge canal was opened at Buffalo, New York, in 1825, a new water highway between New York City and the Great Lakes glistened invitingly in the sun. It was an event of dramatic importance to families and businesses. It meant more goods for consumers, more profits for businessmen. A glorious future seemed at hand.

This was especially true in New York, where people waited anxiously to learn that their long-sought canal was ready at last. The news was to be signaled to them via cannon stationed every few miles along the canal. Men stood with flaming brands poised over their war-like instruments, waiting to relay the glad news to New York.

New York State was like a string of colossal firecrackers waiting to be ignited. The people of the state leaned forward tensely.

Then, in Buffalo, the first fuse burned down to the powder.
BOOM!

Along the canal toward Albany, then down the Hudson toward New York, each cannoneer in turn fired his fuse.
BOOM!
BOOM!

The joyous news crossed the Hudson, passed Tarrytown, Yonkers and rushed toward New York.

At last, from a hilltop near Central Park the final explosion sounded. In the streets of the city, fireworks and whistles long ago made ready now joined the noise and happiness. The canal was open. News of it had reached the city in eighty minutes. Five hundred miles in eighty minutes. Fantastic!

This, in 1825, was considered the ultimate in speed and ease in long distance communication. Nor did the demonstration of Samuel Morse's telegraph before Congress in 1844, disturb it. When Morse offered his invention to the government for $100,000, he was turned down. The skeptical lawmakers saw no future in the telegraph. It would never replace signals relayed from one cannon to another.

By 1877 the mighty Western Union Company had planted its poles all the way to the West Coast, had put the Pony Express out of business, had helped preserve the Union, and had already erected its ruinously tall poles in the streets of New York.

That same year young, struggling Alexander Graham Bell offered his new telephone to Western Union for $100,000. Bell's gimmick, the company judged, would never replace the telegraph. Western Union turned him down.

The telephone was born with problems. For one thing, a person had to shout into it. One didn't begin a conversation with the word "hello." One roared: "AHOY! HOY!" For many years, according to Bell's assistant, Thomas Watson, farmers waiting in a country grocery store would "rush out and hold their horses when they saw anyone preparing to use the telephone."

In attempts to publicize his invention, Bell would give lectures and demonstrations, the climax of which would be Watson bellowing songs into the other end of the wire at the top of his lungs. All the hit-parade favorites of the day were represented at these performances, including such big sellers as "Do Not Trust Them, Gentle Maiden." Though Watson sang so loudly that his voice cracked from the strain, the tune always issued from the receiver torn, frayed and faint.

The first pair of telephones was rented out in May, 1877—two cumbersome contrapations connected by one iron wire which had to be buried in the earth at each end to form a grounded circuit.

The telephone was and is as sensitive and delicate as a cobweb. Grounded in this manner, it picked such a meaningless jangle of noises out of the earth that some users could not hear voices at all. Instead they listened to sounds which sputtered, bubbled, rasped, wheezed and screamed. The rustling of leaves could be heard, the deep, throaty croak of bullfrogs, the clicking of telegraph keys, the flapping of wings. The telephone seemed to pick up every minuscule sound in the county.

"The poor little telephone business," wrote an early observer, "was like a dog with a tin can tied to its tail."

"Perhaps we are picking up signals from Mars," said the whimsical Watson.

At last it was decided that the earth was tainted and could not be used as a ground to complete the connection. A second wire (and wire was horrifyingly expensive to telephone pioneers) had to be twined around the first, and the whole hung from telegraph poles above the streets of the city. There was no thought of burying it in conduits under the pavement. To bury a wire was to smother it—or so men believed in the early days of this new science called "telephony." The wires could not carry sound any distance at all underground, any more than birds could fly underground. Both needed the freedom of the open air.

If all this sounds fanciful, it is nonetheless a true portrait of the infant industry, of a time when an observer could write of the telephone current: "It is perhaps the quickest, feeblest, and most elusive force in the world. . . . It is as gentle as a touch of a baby sunbeam, and as swift as the lightning flash. It is so small that the electric current of a single incandescent lamp is greater five hundred million times. Cool a spoonful of hot water just one degree, and the energy set free by the cooling will operate a telephone for ten thousand years. Catch the falling tear-drop of a child, and there will be sufficient water-power to carry a spoken message from one city to another.

"Such is the tiny Genie of the Wire that had to be protected and trained into obedience. It was the most defenseless of all electric sprites, and it had so many enemies. Enemies! The world was populous with its enemies. There was the lightning, its elder brother, striking at it with murderous blows. There were the telegraphic and light-and-power currents, its strong

and malicious cousins, chasing and assaulting it whenever it
ventured too near. There were rain and sleet and snow and
every sort of moisture, lying in wait to abduct it. There were
rivers and trees and flecks of dust. It seemed as if all the known
and unknown agencies of nature were in conspiracy to thwart
or annihilate this gentle little messenger who had been con-
jured into life by the wizardry of Alexander Graham Bell."

There were also, once the wires had been hung to rooftops
and poles in New York, the chimneys which frayed off insulation, and the damp and rain which soon rusted through the
early iron wire. There were the rooftops themselves which,
since they carried telephone wire, had to be kept in repair, and
the storms which sometimes knocked down in twenty-four hours
enough wires to wipe out a whole year's profit.

For all these reasons, the telephone company knew it had to
go underground; if it didn't municipal authority would soon
force it to anyway. Already the sky above New York was black
with wires, and some poles, like the towering Norway pines
along West Street, were ninety feet high, carried thirty crosstrees and three hundred wires. The people of the city, complaining bitterly, would not stand for much more.

But the telephone did not know how to go underground,
and within the company the old arguments were raised: the
earth was tainted, it smothered sound.

Could an insulation be found to guard the wires?

No one knew, but an experiment had to be tried. A heavy
plow was hauled to a railway track near Boston and hitched to
a locomotive. As the locomotive steamed ahead a furrow was
opened beside the track in deep jerks—though the original
plow had to be replaced by four of its brothers within five
miles, all of them torn to pieces by the mighty locomotive.

In the ditch thus opened, wires insulated in every known
way were laid down, to be smothered by the return of the locomotive towing a great block of wood, which dragged the loose
dirt back into the ditch. The telephone was underground for
the first time.

Some of the insulation used in this experiment worked well
enough to encourage telephone engineers. Accordingly, in
1882, the first cables were laid, one in Boston, the other in

Brooklyn. They worked so well that Watson remarked: "One didn't have to ask the other man to say it over again more than three or four times . . . if the sentences were simple."

In 1883, despite a bombardment of explosions from leaky gas mains, despite makeshift tools, ducts and "experts," the telephone at last submarined under wire-bound New York. It was a complex, arduous task. To serve as conduits, iron pipes were first used, then asphalt, concrete, troughs of sand, and creosoted wood. Each wire was first swathed in cotton, then twisted together with ninety-nine other wires into a cable. The cables were then soaked in oil to eliminate the smallest taint of moisture.

The company kept experimenting. In 1885 a young engineer discovered a machine which would mold liquid lead around a rope of twisted wires. At last cables could be absolutely insulated. Victory over the most malicious enemy of all—moisture—had been achieved. Oil, a dribbling, drooling worker at best, was immediately sacked.

Having made the cable tight, a way was sought to manufacture it more cheaply. What about substituting paper for the cotton with which each strand of wire was wrapped?

This suggestion came from a common laborer, and the machine for winding the paper on wire came from a dress factory, where it had helped in the making of ladies' bonnets. Not all invention is genius. Adjustments were made to this machine, and soon the paper was wound on loosely, even untidily. Oddly enough, the more crumpled the paper, the more sloppily it was applied, the better the wire "talked."

All this was trial and error, the most exasperating kind of scientific research. Equally maddening experiments were made with the wire itself. The primitive glavanized iron was cheap enough, but had no other virtue. It was noisy—conversations fairly crackled across it—and it conducted electric current serviceably, but without enthusiasm.

Steel wire was no better, just more expensive. The ideal wire, it was found at long last, would be wire drawn from silver. Merely to imagine silver wire gave the telephone pioneers the horrors. It was, of course, out of the question. Suppose they did bury silver cables—every night hordes of poor or avaricious men would dig up the graves and make off with long strands of it. No, silver would never have worked, even if enough money could have been found to try it.

Copper was next best, but too soft. Copper was almost as soft as clay and a wire drawn from it would not support its own weight. The problem was: either make steel a better conductor, or strengthen copper.

In a few weeks a young man appeared with a spool of wire in his arms. It was copper, he explained, but a special copper, tough-skinned due to a process he had invented himself.

Before the young man could take off his coat, his wire had been stretched between two chairs, and various objects hung upon it. It supported them all. The spool was rushed outdoors and strung between two poles, then, almost immediately, was strung all the way to Boston. It didn't break at all.

In fact it worked marvelously, far better than any wire yet tried. The men who directed telephone affairs were so pleased that they did not even back off at the wire's price, which was four times that of iron or steel.

"We can always buy some copper mines," remarked one of them. They did, too. Fully a quarter of the company's capital was, by 1900, invested in copper mines.

Meanwhile, corps of human spiders went on spinning their webs beneath the streets of New York. By 1889, the year Mayor Grant ordered the telegraph poles chopped down, eleven thousand miles of telephone wire lay in leaden caskets under the city; every big business soon had a telephone—or perhaps even several, the wire entering through the basement and being fluffed out into various offices, climbing up inside the walls like ivy.

The telephone had got under the city just in time. Had it been born ten years later, had it been buried alongside the powerful trolley and electric cables which were soon to go underground, it could never have survived. Their currents would have drowned it out, overwhelmed its delicate force. By the time the other cables did go under, the telephone was strong enough to defend itself.

At this time, the Consolidated Telegraph and Electric Subway Company had been granted the sole right to dig up the streets of New York. Soon the dainty telephone wires and the muscular electric cables were lying side by side under a blanket of street, strange bedfellows indeed.

Though the telephone could not be overcome by the heavy cables beside it, the clear bell of a voice it had once known, now had a crackle of electricity in it.

The telephone wanted a divorce, and soon got it. A second "subway" company was chartered, the Empire City Subway Company, and into its less noisy house all telephone and telegraph cables quickly moved.

Both subway companies still exist; the one is now a subsidiary of Con Edison, the other a subsidiary of the Telephone Company. Their manhole covers still are emblazoned with the initials of the original subway companies.

Cables still are pushed through tile ducts in the same old way too, sheathed in lead and insulated against moisture forever. After a joint has been made, hot paraffin is poured on to boil out all moisture and air. Then joints are wrapped in muslin and a lead sleeve is slipped into place and soldered at both ends to the lead sheath. So important is an airtight connection that linemen may spend as long as half an hour gently rubbing or "wiping" the hot lead joint to make certain that not a single bubble or pore remains through which air or moisture can enter the cable.

Each cable, incidentally, may contain four thousand or more wires leading, directly or indirectly, to every point on earth. The telephone has come a very long way since the days when Watson used to bellow: "Do Not Trust Them, Gentle Maiden" into one end of the wire, the song trickling tattered and torn from the other end, each word or note a fabulous new experience for all who heard it.

19. The Curious and the Bizarre

Bums, LIKE BIRDS, are migrating creatures who normally go south for the winter. There are exceptions to the rule, of course. Edmund Love, in his book *Subways Are for Sleeping,* told of one enterprising character whose "room rent" came to exactly fifteen cents a night—the price of a subway token. This particular bum knew the routes of all the subway lines, kept his clothes presentable and his routine varied so as not to arouse the suspicions of conductors and/or cops, and managed to nap a total of eight hours every night—with only minor interruptions at the end of the line to change trains. The bum actually enjoyed living that way, enjoyed particularly the illicit smoke in the men's room while waiting for the train to start back the other way. He never boarded a subway except at night; when he wanted to go from one place to another he walked, even to the end of the island. Once Love asked him why he didn't take the subway, it only cost fifteen cents. "Not me," replied the bum. "Subways are for sleeping."

When wintry winds howled through the canyons of the city, another breed of bum, less hardy, more ingenious than the subway-sleepers, searched out a warmer, snugger nest than a drafty subway car—the tight, dark under-street corridors of the New York Steam Company. There are many such corridors under New York, especially near the company's midtown plant. Entrance is via company manholes. The corridors are very narrow; in most of them there is barely enough room for a man and a steam pipe to pass abreast. But it must be admitted that they are warm. To the freezing, probably hungry bum who first discovered them, they must have seemed the cosiest place in town. So he lay down next to a steam pipe, snuggling up to this new wife. She was warmer, and considerably cheaper than any wife he had known before.

In time the news spread through the city's bum colony, and soon there were men camped out beside steam pipes during all the coldest part of the winter.

It was not only warm down there, it was hot. Too hot. Before the winter had ended, several of the bums had perished, cuddled in death with their beloved steam pipes, done in by the terrific heat which had built up during the night. Not till then did the company find out about the dozens of bums who had made homes in its corridors. Those who survived were driven out into the cold again, and it is presumed that most of them resumed the practice of heading for Florida in winter.

The company also took steps to see that its corridors could not be invaded a second time. If you are cold as you read this and have no place to sleep, do not look to the steam company. You cannot get into its manholes any more—or so the company claims, anyway.

As cold and damp as the steam corridors were suffocatingly hot, are the dank, mysterious vaults under the great stone arches of the Brooklyn Bridge. It was as wine cellars that they first came into existence in 1876, seven years before the bridge itself was finished. Dark and gloomy even then, they housed the choicest wines in the city: light, dry Pommards, Chambertins and Châteauneuf-du-Papes from France, brisk Reislings and Moselles from Germany, elegant, sparkling Champagnes. Year after year dust and mold collected on the bottles as they waited in racks to please the palates of the blue bloods of the city. Inside the bottles, the delicate wines aged slowly.

Known as Oech's Wine Cellars, they were famous in New York, and attracted hundreds of visitors annually. People loved to pass through the studded iron doors into the damp, gloomy caves, there to gaze upon the luxurious burden of the moldy racks.

From the damp and closeness, niter collected on the walls, and in the dark gave forth an eerie glow. Someone had placed a stone statue of a blue Madonna in a niche in the vault; she, too, became coated in niter, and in the phosphorescent glow of the dark she seemed to step forward from her niche and float in the air. Few were immune to the spell cast by the Blue Madonna. The devout knelt to her and prayed; the superstitious fled in terror.

With Prohibition, the medieval-like vaults could be wine cellars no longer. During the twenties the city collected its top rent for them, about $73,000 a year—not as wine cellars, but to store fish from the Fulton Fish Market which would go bad if not put on ice overnight. The romantic era was over.

Nowadays the city earns about $25,000 annually in rents, and the vaults are used to store cables, canned goods and bins of rubber heels. Through the narrow streets of this oldest part of the city, great trucks rumble up and depart all day.

Inside, the walls have been whitewashed, but still glitter and glow where the whitewash has peeled away. The Blue Madonna is gone, stolen by a Tammany politician about 1942—no doubt it occupies a place of reverence in his home; it had no intrinsic value. Though the walls are patchy and flaked, painted vine trellises climb one of them to the ceiling. In other places one can just make out words painted there generations ago:

"Who loveth not wine, women and song, he remaineth a fool his whole life long."

And: "The best wine goeth down sweetly, causing the lips of those who are asleep to speak."

One of the world's largest deposits of copper lies under the streets of New York—over three hundred million pounds of pure copper electric cables.

While copper is not indigenous to Manhattan, many other minerals are. The largest garnet crystal found in North America came out of a ditch on Thirty-fifth Street. Finding it was, of course, an accident. Semi-precious stones, even a rich vein of them, cannot be mined. Their value could never equal that of the precious real estate above.

The city did not even stop to mine a deposit of uranium,

although it located so much of the stuff under the West Side Highway that instruments of engineers building the highway were completely disrupted. Even today, if you drive along with a Gieger counter in your car, it will begin clicking as you pass over a certain point.

Unless the structure of New York City should be thoroughly altered (by a bomb blast, for instance) that uranium will lie there forever. The West Side Highway is the aorta of the city's arteries, one of the busiest and most valuable routes in the world.

There are 351 pedestrian tunnels under streets, one of them half a mile long. Some of these pathways are known to many New Yorkers, who use them to escape rain or snow or thick traffic above. Other tunnels seem known only to certain civic authorities and to all bums—bums apparently know everything about New York—who use them to sleep in. The latter variety of tunnels has to be closed between 10:00 P.M. and 6:00 A.M. to exclude such unwelcome visitors.

There are no direction signs along these underground passages, and an apprentice explorer can get bewilderingly lost in no time at all. It is possible, for instance, to walk from Thirty-first Street and Eighth Avenue, to Fortieth Street and Sixth, a distance of twelve blocks, but you had better hire a guide before you try it.

The route starts at Penn Station, drops down past the gates of the Long Island Railroad, then, mounting two flights of stairs, enters a tunnel which leads to Sixth Avenue. There it turns north, passes the turnstiles of the BMT subway, and heads for those of the IND. Don't reach for a token—these turnstiles also are avoided. One merely follows the underground sidewalk which runs all the way up to Fortieth Street.

In many case these passageways came into existence because a subway, for one reason or another, was obliged to burrow deep. Rather than simply fill in the space between the subway and the street, engineers built passageways.

Other passageways, like those under Rockerfeller Center, are narrow corridors plunging past tightly packed tiny shops, the walls as close together as the streets of any medieval village.

Not just anybody can build a passageway under New York. Some years ago Macy's Department Store wanted to link its basement with Penn Station via such a tunnel. But that would have meant submarining under Herald Square, an area so crowded, according to one worker, that "there isn't room to bury a pencil." There certainly wasn't room for Macy's tunnel and the project was abandoned.

The most vulnerable of under-street cables run through ducts whose manholes are double sealed—there's one manhole at street level and a second one twelve inches down. Nothing else is as delicate as telephone lines. Once an entire bank of them was put out of commission because a single termite took a liking to their plastic insulation, and gorged himself to death eating a hole that was no bigger than a pinprick. Not only did dozens of phones go instantly dead, but dozens of repairmen nearly went mad—trying to discover the trouble. How does one find a hole the size of a pinprick, bored by a hungry termite?

In hundreds of different ways men and women make their living underground in New York. At the Columbus Circle subway station alone there is a thriving snack bar, a shop for high-priced candy, a booth making keys, and a stand selling flowers—the carnations wilt swiftly underground and the gilded ferns are really a better buy. There are also several shoeshine stands and paper stands; and men arrive at regular intervals to service the rental lockers and the candy, gum and peanut machines. But Columbus Circle is small time compared to Times Square or Grand Central Station.

But no job underground, or anywhere else for that matter, is as dull as driving the shuttle trains between Times Square and Grand Central. The track is less than half a mile long, top allowable speed is 20 MPH, and the view is not exactly exhilarating. A shuttle motorman makes the trip fifty-six times a day, five days a week. That's fourteen thousand times a year. All he sees is two rails, two signal lights and, as he glides toward the terminus, a sign saying *STOP*.

Nonetheless, one shuttle motorman, spied recently, was as bronzed as an Indian. Where had he acquired his tan?

"I spend my weekends on a farm in Connecticut," he responded. "I sure do like the fresh air up there."

More than a billion gallons of water comes into New York each day—and more than a billion gallons of sewage goes out. The water is easily handled, as has been explained, but the sewage is not so neat a matter. Part of the vast bulk of it goes to treatment plants where it is boiled down to about a thousand solid tons every twenty-four hours, the sewage itself, under treatment, generating enough methane gas to run the plants, the thousand tons being loaded into barges and dumped at sea. Sewage which does not go through the treatment plants is carried through ducts to mid-river so that tidal currents flush it swiftly out to sea.

Sewage has never been a joke to New York. The city was born without sewers and came by them late in life via the school of hard knocks. The first real sewers were not built until after Croton water came in—beginning about 1850. They were haphazardly made, did not drain well, and soon the whole city stank from them. This caused the ingenious Common Council to order buckets of perfume poured down sewers in a foolish attempt to sweeten the smell.

The first sewers led to cesspools which leaked; further poisoning the soil and wells of the city. Then they were carried in great trunk lines which emptied directly into the rivers where, it was decided, municipal responsibility ended.

So by 1890 the harbor and bay of New York, shimmering in the noonday sun, stank mightily. More than one boatload of immigrants sailed up the Hudson with handkerchiefs pressed to noses, having received an "overpowering" first impression of the Land of Opportunity.

Near-by beaches were not safe. Citizens unwise enough to swim off them came away with skin rashes. Some swallowed water, became ill, died.

It was the contaminated beaches which led to the birth of the treatment plants to tone down sewage which at times could be as deadly as pure poison. Before long, not a single gallon of sewage will pass into the Atlantic without having been treated first.

But for the present, contaminated beaches are still an occasional hazard near New York. The health department is still researching the problem. One August day in 1956 it launched three hundred sealed bottles, with bright flags sticking out of the corks, at various sewer outlets along the perimeter of Manhattan. The bottles contained postcards addressed to the department, and the labels on the bottles bore instructions. Finders were requested to withdraw the postcards, write when, where and how they had found the drifting bottles, and mail the cards. By compiling this information, the department hoped to increase its knowledge of local tides and currents. A thorough publicity campaign urged vacationers to watch out for the bottles, 158 of which turned up at various city beaches by August 26, each informing a blissfully unaware swimmer that the patch of "seaweed" floating near by, was not seaweed at all. There is no evidence that the bottles performed any other function.

Part of the patois of underground New York is the term "Vegetable Charley." Actually, an underground worker seems to feel a bit contemptuous of Vegetable Charleys, because they are not underground workers at all. A Vegetable Charley is a man who patrols the streets of the city looking for bits of discolored vegetation—a few blades of crab grass pushing up through the crack between the curb and the street, perhaps.

Natural gas, a comparative newcomer to the city, will wither and discolor plant life on contact, but it is so nearly odorless that it is difficult to detect when leaking. A few blades of grass can tell a Vegetable Charley that a gas main under the street is cracked and that gas he can't smell is seeping out of it. Those few blades of grass, plus Vegetable Charleys, save both gas and lives.

The New York subways were scheduled for spring cleaning in 1959, after having gone fifty-five years without a bath.

It was a bath which would cost $33,000 for "scrubbing brushes" alone. No one could say the lady didn't need it. She was filthy. The station platforms had been swept during the past half century. Debris such as discarded tabloids and chewing-gum wrappers had been regularly collected from the tracks.

But the tunnels themselves were caked with grime an inch thick. Each time a train rushed through a tunnel, the column of air behind it would stir up dust—dust impregnated with metallic bits and shavings rubbed off wheels and rails over the years. This metallic dust got into the engines and brakes of trains following, and caused excessive wear, needless breakdowns.

It also got into the noses and lungs of passengers, who began to complain with increasing bitterness of respiratory ailments brought on by a dirty subway.

So at last the Transit Authority weakened. The tunnels were to be returned to their pristine beauty. Four used tank cars were bought from the Marshall Railway Equipment Company.

"They will do the job as well as new ones," explained the Transit Authority. "After all, the lady isn't young any more."

Four hydraulic steam cleaners also were purchased. Men mounted on the tank cars would hose down the walls of the tunnel with hard jets of live steam. Under the battering pressure of the steam (made from water mixed with detergent) the scum and caked dirt of the tunnels would disintegrate and fall to the track bed. From there hoses would flush it way in the normal manner.

The job would take fifteen months. Tunnels that had been black would be white again—at which point motormen could be expected to begin complaining about the glare.

You can't please all of the people . . .

As for the tracks and platforms themselves, it takes eighty men and $330,000 a year to keep them even as clean as they are. This is not all due to those carelessly dropped newspapers and chewing-gum wrappers.

The oil and grease which dribbles from the great wheels and engines of the trains, one drop at a time, amounts to eleven thousand tons in a year. This must be scraped off every six months—otherwise the grit and sludge would in time rise above the level of the tracks, and the trains would soon be plowing through it like snow. In the busier stations—those served by both local and express trains, by two or more lines—six months is too long and the grit and sludge must be scraped off and carried away every three months.

About five hundred tons of gum wrappers and other paper is removed from the tracks each year, and is promptly sold to junk and used-paper dealers. The tracks at stations are cleared of debris once a week where traffic is light, twice a week at midtown and other heavily used stops.

This work goes on round the clock, except during rush hours. Late at night ghost trains glide silently into stations. They are dark, empty, and their destination windows are blank, like turned-up sightless eyes. One door opens, a man steps out, grasps sacks of rubbish which lie ready for him on the platform, and drags them back to the dead train. The door closes again, and the train moves on to the next station.

Afternoon, night, dawn—all are the same underground, particularly to the men who clean the subways, who try to stay abreast of the gum wrappers, the tattered tabloids, the dripping oil. Theirs is a war that can never be won.

The above facts, and certain others in this book, were supplied by the Transit Authority's six-person public relations bureau. This bureau came into existence in 1955 at a time when the subways had, it was judged, fewer friends than at any time in their history.

The bureau has many duties, most of them unsuspected by those who ride the subways. It issues a poster called "The Subway Sun," which is pasted to train windows and which contains such helpful hints as how to avoid rush-hour crowding (you take the local, of course) or gives direction (by subway, of course) to Rockaway Beach. It writes speeches for Transit Authority bigwigs. It sends out news releases. It answers complaints from riders. Most of all it keeps a complete listing of all delays so that workers, late to the office, can suggest that irate or doubting bosses check their alibis. Sometimes this "alibi" service saves jobs, sometimes it loses them. For there is an occasional rider who is not aware of the service, working for a boss who is—and who takes the trouble to check. Just another of life's two-edged swords.

Under Brooklyn's Atlantic Avenue, from Boerum Place to Emmett Street, there is a tunnel seventeen feet high, twenty-one feet wide, half a mile long and completely empty. It is said that nature abhors a vacuum. So does a city, for the paraphernalia of living is so strewn about that eventually, like water, it overflows into every usable nook and cranny. Nothing stays vacant long.

Therefore it is incredible that this tunnel has been sealed up since 1861. In all that time there has never been a serious attempt to make it serve a legitimate purpose. (It has been used illegitimately, of course.) Year after year the tunnel just lies there, under one of Brooklyn's busiest thoroughfares. In time, no doubt, it will be forgotten completely.

With it will be forgotten the smugglers, saboteurs, murderers and clandestine mushroom growers who have been hunted in there during the twentieth century, as well as the sedate and prosperous Brooklyn of 1836, which had a curious vision of the future, and which first ordered the tunnel built.

The city counted a population of about forty thousand that year. It was a proud and elegant place and the men who directed its affairs had already determined that it would grow into a great and beautiful metropolis. Atlantic Avenue was to be the hub, its Broadway, its Champs Elysée. Atlantic Avenue was to be tree-lined, wide, gorgeous. But Atlantic Avenue also stood in the way of the Long Island Railroad which crossed Brooklyn to get to the harbor at the foot of the East River.

The railroad had to go through. Atlantic Avenue had to stay beautiful.

There was only one thing to do, drop the tracks twenty feet below street level so that the coal-burning blunderbusses which served as locomotives could be heard but not seen.

Small though it was, Brooklyn was a city with a dream and did not count this scheme too ambitious. The cut was finished January 1, 1845. Five years later a "sturdy brick arch" was placed over it and the tunnel was complete.

"The tunnel is a work of art which will forever embellish the

city of Brooklyn," intoned George Fisk, president of the railroad, at the opening ceremonies.

The chaste good looks of Atlantic Avenue were preserved,
even as trains roared by underfoot.

But the dream died young.

Because the locomotives of the day burned coal, and spewed
sparks and cinders in all directions, there had to be openings
in the roof to permit the smoke and gases to escape. Unfortunately, what spouted out of the vents, showered down upon
the swank homes of Brooklyn Heights. On the Heights, their
mansions overlooking New York Harbor and the upper bay,
lived the wealthiest and most influential citizens of Brooklyn.
To them the purity of their own homes soon seemed more
important than the purity of Atlantic Avenue.

In the courts a running battle began to be fought between
residents of Brooklyn Heights, people with wealth and prestige,
and those of the rest of Brooklyn, some of whom were hard-
working, poor and sustained by little more than their dream
of a beautiful city.

At last in 1858, an impartial court in White Plains, New
York, ordered that wood-or coal-burning locomotives be pro-
hibited from entering the city of Brooklyn, that the nuisance
of the showering sparks and cinders be lifted from the residents
of Brooklyn Heights.

There was nothing to do with the tunnel now but to close
it. Accordingly, in 1861, it was sealed up. It has stayed sealed
ever since.

To be sure, occasional sunlight has trickled in through rup-
tures of its skin. But mostly the years have served merely to
swath the tunnel in layer after layer of legend.

It is said, for instance, that smugglers got into it shortly
after the Civil War, bringing contraband up from the bay in
small boats, and storing it there. The tunnel was not completely
closed at the time, according to this tale, and the police were
obliged to go down and shoot it out with the smugglers. Much
honest blood was shed as a result, the smugglers having built
veritable fortress walls, behind which in the dark they were
able to take pot shots at the descending cops who were framed
in the light from above.

Finally, it is said, the police tired of the unequal game, sealed all the entrances and left the smugglers in there to rot.

Like most of the yarns surrounding the Atlantic Avenue tunnel, there is no way of knowing if this story is true or not. For many years it was claimed that an old wood-burning locomotive still stood on its rails in the tunnel, but an exploration about 1910 proved this a fiction. There was nothing at all in there but a few decaying boards, it was reported. There were not even any corpses or bones.

Better substantiated is the story of an enterprising chap who cut into the tunnel from his basement and grew mushrooms in there, about 1920. This man had the misfortune to chose a period in history when the tunnel was also being used by saloon owners along Atlantic Avenue for the manufacture of illicit bourbon, the booze actually being piped up into the bars, where glasses of the thirsty would be filled at perfectly innocent-looking faucets.

Detectives found and rooted out all of these stills before long, the mushroom grower with them, and the tunnel was again sealed.

It next entered the news in 1936, when Acting Captain John J. McGowan of the police department received a tip that one Bo Weinberg, a notorious hoodlum, had been murdered and that the tunnel was his crypt.

McGowan and four detectives spent several days rooting about in garbage and rat-infested cellars along Atlantic Avenue, searching for just one of the reputed "twenty secret entrances" to the tunnel. But they found no trace of any. At length a truckload of laborers and pneumatic jackhammers were sent round and a crude, non-secret entrance was chewed through the street into the roof of the tunnel.

After all that work, McGowan, too, discovered that legend is a powerful thing. There was no hoodlum in the tunnel, dead or otherwise. There was nothing in the tunnel at all, although to search there had seemed perfectly reasonable at the start.

(Weinberg later turned up in a barrel of cement in Buffalo.)

The tunnel was opened briefly in 1941, when WPA laborers examined it to see if the roof was strong enough to continue to support so much traffic. Having proved that it was, they closed the tunnel and went away. A few years later some F.B.I. agents opened it again, having received a tip that it was headquarters for German saboteurs. This investigation added considerably to the tunnel's burden of legend, but not at all to the bureau's bag of spies.

From time to time the tunnel still is in the news, usually when being proposed as a possible parking lot to ease Brooklyn's massive traffic congestion. The proposal always sounds like a new idea, and a good one, until it is pointed out that the tunnel, though wide enough for two "monstrous" wood-burning locomotives to run side by side in the early nineteenth century, is barely as wide as a modern car is long. No 1959 Cadillac or Chrysler could possibly turn around down there.

And so the the tunnel stays empty and dark, occupied only by its legends. No one has been in there since the last F.B.I. agent during the war. Nor is anyone likely to enter it during the next hundred years.

Unless perhaps it's a smuggler, a murderer or a saboteur.

20. A Building Goes Up— and Down

As THE TOWER of each new skyscraper rises to prod the sky above New York, the under-street problems become more and more complex. The sixty-story Chase Manhattan Building has been planted a hundred feet down—not to satisfy an engineer's yearning for the spectacular, but because that's how deep drillers had to bore to find rock solid enough to support the building's ponderous bulk. So heavy is the building that it will be balanced not upon bare bedrock, but atop forty steel blocks weighing forty tons each, blocks which were lowered gently into the hole by a mighty derrick which itself stood nine stories high, weighed seventy tons and which looked as awkward and overbalanced as some colossal giraffe, the cables in its neck standing out from the strain.

Engineers erecting the Union Carbide Building on Park Avenue piecrust faced an even stiffer test. The stilts of that structure, which is to rise fifty-two stories by 1960, thrust down through the piecrust piercing two levels of New York Central track in their drive to root in bedrock. The job was fantastically complicated. First the old Marguery Hotel, a New York landmark since 1917, had to be torn down and the girders on which it stood removed, all without disturbing the six hundred daily Central trains or their tracks. By today's standards, the Marguery was a modest building, only thirteen stories high. But still its girders—there were nearly a hundred of them—were as much

214

Jerry Dantzic

New York can go higher and deeper. . . .

as sixty feet long and weighed sixty tons. Vertical girders were cut through at the base by acetylene torches, then yanked out of the ground like diseased teeth by giant cranes. Horizontal girders were lowered onto flatcars and hauled from the tunnel by locomotives, to be disposed of more easily in a less cramped place. Other debris from the Marguery demolition, about two hundred tons of it a day, also was removed via flatcars.

When nothing but memory was left of the Marguery, engineers faced the task of jockeying newer, longer, wider, heavier girders down through the train rooms again, scraping past some tracks with only inches to spare. This work was so intricate and difficult, and crammed the train rooms so full of men and machines, that much of it could be done only at night when even a railroad is quiet and napping.

At bedrock the tremendous shafts were nine-feet square, stood upon asbestos-lead vibration mats, and were cushioned on all sides by cork. "We can't have a fifty-two-story building vibrating with each incoming train," explained one official.

Most of what goes on underground is as private as what takes place in a boudoir. But this building flaunted her nakedness in plain view. Thousands of pedestrians peered down at her through the sudden gap in the Park Avenue piecrust. Thousands more looked upon her bare bones as their trains filed slowly by, every morning and evening. This was a girl who had no secrets at all.

When finished she will have cost something like $47,000,000 and will shelter five thousand industrious persons. All of them will have to walk up one flight to catch the elevator—it starts on the second floor. Some of an elevator's machinery in a building so massive, must be housed in a fifteen-foot box below the bottom stop. To start this one at ground level would have meant dropping the machinery box directly into the path of the New York Central's crack Chicago express, because the piecrust, there as elsewhere, is only six inches thick. This the railroad executives decided against.

New buildings, big or little, must all eventually be hooked up to cables, pipes, mains and wires. Which connection is made first? "Contractors always hook up with sewers first," declares a sewer official. "Then if they should cut into some spring or stream they didn't know about, they have some place to pump the water. They hook up with sewers first. They're not supposed to, but they all do it."

Sewers, on the average, are thirteen feet below street level. All other utilities are about four feet down, deep enough so that they will not freeze, no matter what the temperature above, shallow enough so that they are accessible in emergencies.

Anybody who owns a pneumatic jackhammer can cut through the crust of the island in a few minutes. The city's ganglia is only a few spadefuls of earth below that. It is of course illegal to break up streets without a permit, but this did not stop some college boys from roping off a section of Times Square and digging their own private excavation as a prank. When they judged that the hole was deep enough, they simply piled into their borrowed truck and drove away. They were never caught. The city later filled in the hole. It is to be assumed that the cop on the beat was severely disciplined for having permitted such an atrocity to happen—and in Times Square of all places. But how was he to suspect that this was not simply one of the thousands of legal ditches which score New York every year?

At that the college boys were lucky. Digging in New York is not a joke. Not long ago an experienced Empire City Subway Company worker, part of a gang laying new ducts, leaned on the jarring handles of his jackhammer and watched its steel tooth bite into the asphalt surface of the street. A moment later he was dead. The jackhammer had chewed into a 13,000-volt electrical cable which wasn't supposed to be there. The current had shot up the heavy tool into his body. He was dead before he could let go.

Midtown New York has been virtually reconstructed during the last ten years. But for giant scientific advances under the city, this would not have been possible.

Consolidated Edison learned to manage its current at higher voltage than ever before, built several midtown sub-stations to store and/or transform it, and upped wall outlet voltage to

265/460 in many new buildings. By converting to natural gas, which has twice the heat content of manufactured gas, the capacity of the company's gas system was automatically double.

Steam pipes have been reinforced, pressure boosted, tighter insulation found, and new methods developed for using the same steam twice to heat new skyscrapers—at high pressure up to the fourteenth floor, and at reduced pressure above.

The Telephone Company continues to toil over and improve its cables. At present it is using a cable which contains 4,242 wires but is no thicker than the old 1,800 wire cable—about the diameter of a man's wrist.

Even in the sewers, time marches on. More and more treatment plants are being built; before long all New York sewage will pass through them and the waters which bathe the city will be clean. Intricate machines have been devised to pound new sewer pipes before burial, so that those liable to break will be rejected beforehand. Scientists are even working on means of hastening the decomposition of waste by atomic energy.

New subway cars, costing $106,000 each, have been ordered; they will be handsomer, more durable and faster by far than the awkward monster which thundered through the first tunnel under the hand of Mayor McClellan in 1904.

Progress is a combination of genius plus tricks, especially under the streets. New steam lines are laid in pre-fab sections, including insulation and concrete casing, and are welded together in the trench. When antique gas mains break, smaller, stronger new ones are pushed through the old, one section after the other, from a single opening in the street. It saves ripping out the old mains, it saves ripping up more than a short stretch of street, and nothing is lost in gas because the new main is stouter and pressure can be increased. Most of all, these new methods are quick.

Similarly, the Telephone Company sometimes sinks pre-fab manholes. It lays 4,242 wire cables where a smaller cable would suffice, so that additional wires will be ready should any new tower be built. It takes advantage of streets ripped up for some other purpose to insinuate more modern equipment or additional, precautionary ducts.

Other tricks help the companies smell approaching trouble. "We can't," says a Con Edison official, "dig up our cables just to see how they are doing." So high voltage lines (and some telephone cables, too) contain insulating oil under pressure. A drop in pressure indicates a leak, and an intense search for it is immediately launched.

All the systems are amazingly integrated. A break in the electrical circuit might plunge no more than a single street light into darkness—because the current is instantly fed in from some other direction. Every generating plant in the city might sink into the rivers, but the great neon signs above Times Square would blaze just as fiercely—on electricity called in from as distant a point as Niagara Falls.

Water is the same. Let City Tunnel No. 1 become clogged at Columbus Circle. Would the lower half of the island go thirsty? Not at all. Tunnel No. 2 could still supply it, the water coursing down through Queens and into Brooklyn, then turning abruptly north into Manhattan.

Telephones are the same, and even gas. If the natural gas which heats some of the city and cooks most of its food (and which comes from Texas) died out to the merest wisp, New Yorkers could still dine on a well-turned roast, or even commit suicide by sticking their heads in ovens. For stand-by plants are ready at any moment to begin manufacturing gas in the same way they did a generation ago, or a century ago.

Danger of subterranean overcrowding is, at present, fairly remote. Both Con Edison and the Telephone Company are at least five years ahead of the city in development. That is, there is duct and cable space ready for at least that much anticipated growth. They are working constantly to stay ahead.

"We can't," noted a Telephone executive, "rip up midtown New York every time a new building goes up!"

To this New Yorkers, inching busily around excavation after excavation, mutter bitterly: "It only seems that way."

There seems only one more objection to be stated—the fear of the very young and the very old that New York can go higher and deeper only so much longer, that eventually the city will be so heavy that the island will sink under it.

Rest easy, son, grandma. There is nothing to worry about. The steel and concrete rising into the sky is heavy, but it can never equal the weight of dirt and rock which has been dug and blasted and gouged out of countless excavations over the years.

New York City weighed more on the day Peter Minuet bought it from the Indians for a handful of beads and trinkets said to be worth $24.

How This Book
Was Written

WHEN THE DAY finally comes that he can lug his manuscript into the publisher's office, drop it on a desk and walk out done with it forever, every author feels profound, sometimes overwhelming relief. Never need he work on *that* again. But an author also feels deeply grateful to all who helped him, and he knows that, even if he sends round a hundred autographed copies of the book when it appears, he can never repay the debt he owes.

All books are the product of many persons. This one was no exception. It began with an idea. Could a book be written on what was under New York? I was frankly skeptical. I went first to Julie Geller, one of the custodians of the New York *Times* morgue. What kind of files were available which would help me? In a few minutes Julie came back with thick folders on explosions and eruptions in the streets. I was encouraged to go on. That was the start.

Next, one goes to the Public Library and pores through the card index under such subject headings as Sewers, Rapid Transit (the generic name for subways), Telephony, Water Supply and Gas. One spends the better part of a week jotting down names and titles. Most of these works are scholarly tomes, or technical ones, or pamphlets written dryly and inexpertly by politicians. One begins to slog through book after book making notes. Gradually one pieces together the skeleton of the story.

More importantly, one stumbles upon vague references to dramatic tales—the Beach Pneumatic Subway, for instance. It is mentioned in all the early books on New York transportation, but is always dismissed quickly as a wild scheme which didn't work. But one book mentions the date of Beach's death, and a check of the microfilms in the New York *Times* turns up his obituary. Beach's *Scientific American* is still being published. I called to ask if they had information on him, plus back issues eighty or ninety years old. No one there knew anything about Beach, and the back issues had been turned over to the Public Library decades ago. Was it possible the library still had them? It did, and I read through volumes brittle with age and, at length, had the whole story.

Another dramatic tale was the brusque removal of the city's telegraph and light poles in 1889. That was recent enough to look for in the *Times* microfilm. And so I read each day's account of the chopping, and soon had a chapter of comedy which resulted in death.

I suppose in all I searched through a hundred books to gather the material in this one. I also examined morgue files at the New York *Daily News*, *Daily Mirror* and *Herald Tribune*. Carrie Quigley, kind and generous as always, helped at the *News*.

Much of the material on the sewers was provided by James P. Lundy, an ex-superintendent, whom I had known many years. It was he who first told me about Teddy May, the man who loved sewers. Mr. Lundy and I sat on his lawn sipping drinks all one summer afternoon while he recounted Teddy May stories. It was funny and touching, and I hope the chapter on Teddy is too.

Mr. Lundy also furnished Teddy's address. Teddy and I met outside the United Cigar Store on Forty-second Street, and had a long chat sitting on a stoop along that street where Teddy was born and has lived all his life. Later Teddy lent me his map of the sewers. "He must have liked you," Mr. Lundy said when I told him this. "I never heard of him letting that out of his possession before."

Two men were writing columns on New York when I started

this book, Sid Fields in the *Mirror*, and Meyer Berger in the *Times*. Harold Weissman introduced me to Mr. Fields and when I told him of the book I was doing he said: "Do you have anything in it on Smelly Kelly? No? What about the rats under the Park Avenue Piecrust?" Thanks to Mr. Fields those subjects too are treated herein.

Mr. Berger, who died last winter, was one of the kindest, most gentle men who ever lived. He would talk to me for hours about New York, about the vaults under the Brooklyn Bridge, the bums suffocating in the steam corridors, the alligators in the sewers. He was one of those I hoped would accept an autographed copy of this book when it was finished, for he helped immeasurably in writing it.

Other friends kept calling up with ideas during all that fall and winter, Frank Corbin, Don Smith, Kyle Rote and my brother Kevin. A. C. Smith of the Telephone Company helped, as did Chuck Hoppin of Con Edison and Eileen Walsh of the Transit Authority. Chester Lewis was kind enough to let me use the *Times* morgue and library; I was not working for the *Times* then, but for Jack and Well Mara whom I also wish to thank as some of this book was written on their time.

It is true that no man is an island. Particularly a writer who hopes to write things other people will read.